FOREWORD – THIRD EDITION

The Civil Engineering Specification for the Water Industry (CESWI) was first published in July 1978, followed by a second edition in August 1984. It is the standard document for civil engineering contracts let by the water authorities of England and Wales, and by bodies such as district councils acting on their behalf for sewerage functions. It is also used by water companies.

In 1987 it was decided to initiate a national survey to elicit comments on how the second edition of the Specification might be improved. Announcements were subsequently made in appropriate publications and comments were invited from within the water industry.

The principal changes reflect the publication since 1984 of revised editions of several documents to which reference is made. Notable among these are the British Standard codes of practice for the structural use of concrete and the design of concrete structures for retaining aqueous liquids; also the Department of Transport's specification for highway works.

In October 1988 the water industry launched its own certification scheme (WICS), to enable products not covered by a British Standard (and therefore unable to be Kitemarked) to be independently certified by application of the 'Watermark'. Such products are manufactured to water industry specifications used by WICS for the purposes of assessing product conformity. Section 2 of the Specification has therefore been extended to reflect the launch of WICS.

Account has been taken of the 1988 European Court of Justice Judgement in the case of the EC versus Ireland, in which it was held that the Treaty of Rome obliged Member States not to preclude consideration of products manufactured to specifications other than their own. The wording of the Specification is also consistent with the UK's interpretation of the requirements of the proposed EC Construction Products Directive.

In response to many requests a further section has been added to the Specification, covering fundamental requirements for sewer renovation works carried out under the ICE Conditions of Contract. The section has also been drafted to be compatible with the sewer renovation class of the Civil Engineering Standard Method of Measurement.

Whilst this edition of the Specification was in draft, the Water Bill was presented to Parliament. The Bill includes proposals for water and sewerage undertakers to submit to the Secretary of State for approval, codes of practice with respect to the exercise of undertakers' pipe-laying powers. Assuming Parliament approves these proposals, it is likely that such codes of practice will include some matters at present covered in this Specification. Accordingly no revisions have been made in this repect to Section 1 of the Specification.

As with previous editions it is envisaged that it will often be necessary to include additional clauses to provide for individual features and the need for such clauses has again been allowed for in the system of numbering. The system should be followed when numbering any additional clauses in order to maintain consistency of presentation.

The Specification was reviewed and redrafted by the following Working Group:

H White	Yorkshire Water (Chairman)
R E Smith	WRc, Swindon (Secretary)
B A Bailey	Welsh Water
Z S Cherryson	Southern Water
F M Firth	Yorkshire Water
P G Homersham	Thames Water
J F Huckerby	Colne Valley Water Company (representing the Water Companies Association)
M J Lee	Wessex Water
S Marques	North West Water
P D Mitchell	Severn Trent Water
I D Moorhouse	Northumbrian Water
I E Reynolds	South West Water*
B E Spark	Anglian Water

* until April 1988

CONTENTS

COMPLIANCE WITH BRITISH STANDARDS

1. Wherever there is an appropriate British Standard or equivalent, the Specification demands that materials and products should comply with its relevant provisions; they must also be Kitemarked if such products are available, though the mark of conformity of any other third party certification body accredited by the National Accreditation Council for Certification Bodies or equivalent is an acceptable alternative to this requirement. This approach is consistent with that agreed by the former NWC Directors of Operations Group, whereby the water industry would seek to improve those Standards with which it was concerned, rather than specifying additional or amended requirements, and would give its full support to BSI certification schemes (see Note 2 below). Water industry representation at BSI is co-ordinated by the WAA Sewers and Water Mains Committee.

2. A British Standard will not normally be available in the case of newly-developed products, but this is not to be seen as inhibiting their use. Water Industry specifications issued by the Sewers and Water Mains Committee deal with products such as these and are called up in the Specification.

3. In references to BS codes of practice, a distinction has been drawn between those which comprise, in the main, standards of good workmanship practice — these are called up in the main text of the Specification — and those which deal largely with matters such as temporary works which are the contractor's responsibility under Clause 8 of the Fifth Edition, which are referred to in the Notes for Guidance.

4. The water industry has agreed with BSI Quality Assurance, Certification and Assessment that its representatives will bring to the attention of the Head of Department (Building and Construction) any problems or complaints experienced with Kitemark certified products. Similarly in respect of products required to comply with a Water Industry specification, any problem or complaint should be brought to the attention of the Manager of the Water Industry Certification Scheme. The manager of any other appropriate certification body should be approached in respect of any complaint relative to a product supplied to an equivalent specification. A sample of the questionnaire to be used is given in Appendix XI. A copy of each completed questionnaire should be sent to the head office of the relevant water authority, marked for the attention of its BSI Liaison Officer. This procedure is not intended to affect the provisions of the Contract.

GENERAL NOTES

 1. The following principles have been followed in drafting the original and successive editions of the Specification:

(i) The Specification is written primarily in terms of the performance required, leaving the Contractor, so far as possible, free to decide his method of working.

(ii) The document is intended for use with the Fifth Edition of the ICE Conditions of Contract and so, in accordance with Clause 5 of those Conditions, provisions already covered by them are excluded from the Specification. For example, such phrases as 'to the satisfaction (or approval) of the Engineer' have been omitted, being covered by Clause 13(1) of the Fifth Edition.

(iii) The Specification is intended for use in conjunction with the Civil Engineering Standard Method of Measurement (CESMM) and the order of subjects follows the same sequence as closely as the scope of the two documents allows.

(iv) There is no reference in the Specification either to the method of assessing payment or to whether the Employer or the Contractor should bear specific costs; these matters are left for inclusion in the Bill of Quantities and its Preamble.

(v) References to Acts of Parliament and other Statutory Instruments are omitted from the main text (though not from the Notes for Guidance and Associated Topics), since the Contractor's compliance with them is a requirement of Clause 26(2) of the Fifth Edition.

(vi) Traditional requirements which are desirable but impossible to achieve in a literal sense have been omitted (e.g. 'pipes to be laid true to line and level').

2. Notes for Guidance are printed in the margins beside the text to which they refer and are designed primarily to assist those preparing contract documents. One of their main purposes is to explain apparent omissions from the text such as those referred to in Note 1 above and to cross refer to other documents (Fifth Edition etc.) where such matters are covered.

3. The 'Associated Topics' listed after Sections 1, 3, 5, 6 and 7 serve the same general purpose as the Notes for Guidance and differ from them only in that they do not relate directly to the printed clauses. In most cases they help to explain why such clauses were omitted.

4. Acts of Parliament, Statutory Instruments and other documents quoted in the marginal Notes for Guidance and the accompanying 'Associated Topics' are those in force at the time of publication.

5. References to Clause numbers in the main text and in the marginal Notes for Guidance relate to Clause numbers of this Specification.

Feedback Arrangements

Any suggestion for amendment of the Specification should be sent to the Water Authorities Association, 1 Queen Anne's Gate, London SW1H 9BT.

Any clauses in this Specification which relate to work or materials not required by the Works shall be deemed not to apply.

The General Notes, clause headings, marginal Notes for Guidance and the accompanying 'Associated Topics' are not part of the Specification, and are not to affect the interpretation either of the Specification or of the other Contract documents.

SECTION 1

GENERAL

1.1 ENTRY ONTO THE SITE

1. Prior to the commencement of operations, the Engineer shall supply to the Contractor the names and addresses of relevant owners and occupiers. The Contractor shall notify the Engineer in writing 14 days in advance of his intention to start work within each area of ownership or occupation.

2. The Contractor shall keep records of the dates of his entry onto and departure from all property and lands of each owner and occupier, together with the dates of the erection and removal of all enclosures, and shall furnish copies of these records when required by the Engineer. He shall keep, and furnish, copies of similar records in respect of roads, footpaths and thoroughfares.

1.2 SURVEY OF HIGHWAYS, PROPERTIES, LANDS AND CROPS

1. Where appropriate, the Engineer shall arrange for surveys to be carried out, in conjunction with the Contractor and the Highway Authority, owners or occupiers, of the condition of highways, properties, lands and crops which may be affected by the Works.

2. Before any work affecting such highways, properties, lands or crops is commenced, the Contractor shall confirm in writing to the Engineer that the relevant survey is a true and accurate record of their condition.

1.3 SITE FENCING

1. Where the type and locations of temporary site fencing are described in the Contract, the Contractor shall erect such fencing as soon as he is given possession of the relevant portion of the Site. The Contractor shall regularly inspect and maintain all such fencing, any defects being made good without delay. Access shall be provided in temporary site fencing as necssary for the use of the occupiers of adjacent lands. Temporary site fencing shall remain in position until either it is replaced by permanent fencing or the Works are sufficiently completed to enable that portion of the Site to be brought into use.

1.4 LEVELS AND REFERENCE POINTS

1. The Contractor shall supply to the Engineer details of the value and location of the temporary bench marks and reference points which he proposes to use.

2. The Contractor shall satisfy himself that the existing ground levels as indicated in the Contract are correct. Should the Contractor wish to dispute any levels he shall submit to the Engineer a schedule of the position of the levels considered to be in error and a set of revised levels. The existing ground relevant to the disputed levels shall not be disturbed before the Engineer's decision as to the correct levels is given.

1.5 ACCOMMODATION FOR THE ENGINEER

1. The Contractor shall provide, heat, light, clean and maintain, until the completion of the Works, accommodation as described in the Contract for the sole use of the Engineer. Offices and other accommodation shall be erected, furnished, equipped and ready for occupation and use within 7 days of the Date for Commencement of the Works, and fully serviced within 28 days of that Date.

2. Where movable offices are required by the Contract, these shall be relocated from time to time as directed by the Engineer.

(iii) For the removal of accommodations, see Clause 33 of the Fifth Edition.

(iv) If required, insurance of office contents should be a Special Condition of Contract.

3. Where the Contract requires telephone facilities for the Engineer, such facilities shall have separate connection direct to a public telephone exchange with privacy of conversation for the Engineer.

(i) Consent of the Local Planning Authority may be required for billposting or advertising.

1.6 BILLPOSTING AND ADVERTISING

1. The Contractor shall not undertake or allow billposting or advertising of any kind upon the Works without the written consent of the Engineer.

(i) Clause 42(2) of the Fifth Edition deals with the provision by the Contractor of any additional land or interests which he may require for the purposes of the Works.

(ii) Section 48 of the Wildlife and Countryside Act 1981 imposes a statutory duty on water authorities to "further the conservation and enhancement of natural beauty and the conservation of flora, fauna and geological or physiological features of special interest" when carrying out their works. Any special precautions necessary to comply with the provisions of the Act should be described in the Contract.

1.7 INTERFERENCE WITH LAND INTERESTS

1. The Contractor shall confine his constructional operations within the Site, or such other areas of land as may be negotiated, and shall instruct his employees not to trespass.

2. Subject to any unavoidable disturbance which may be necessitated by the execution of the Contract, the Contractor shall not interfere with any sporting, fishing or other rights which may be enjoyed on or near the Site.

3. Before exercising any right negotiated by him in connection with wayleaves or accommodation outside the Site, the Contractor shall notify the Engineer in writing of such arrangements.

(i) For requirements that the Contractor shall not interfere unnecessarily with access, see Clause 29(1) of the Fifth Edition.

1.8 INTERFERENCE WITH ACCESS TO PROPERTIES AND SERVICES

1. Before interfering with access to any property, the Contractor shall provide alternative arrangements. The Contractor shall notify the Engineer and the relevant occupiers in writing 14 days in advance of any such interference and shall confirm to the Engineer that alternative arrangements have been agreed.

2. The Contractor shall not obstruct access to any Public Utility or privately owned manhole or other surface cover.

(i) This Clause will assist in the operation of Clause 22 of the Fifth Edition by ensuring that all parties are aware of any difficulties which may have arisen during the Contract.

1.9 PROCEDURE FOR COMPLAINTS AND CLAIMS FOR DAMAGE

1. Details of all claims or warnings of intended claims which the Contractor may receive in respect of matters against which he is required by the Contract to indemnify the Employer shall be notified without delay to the Engineer, who shall likewise pass to the Contractor any such claims or warnings which may be submitted directly to the Engineer or Employer.

2. A similar exchange of information shall also be made in relation to all complaints which may be received.

3. The Contractor shall notify the Engineer in writing immediately following any damage or injury arising out of the execution of the Works.

(i) This Clause refers to the avoidance of damage. See Clause 22(1) of the Fifth Edition for liabilities following the occurrence of any damage.

(ii) For the avoidance and consequences of damage to highways by 'extraordinary traffic', see Clause 30 of the Fifth Edition.

1.10 PROTECTION AGAINST DAMAGE

1. The Contractor shall take all necessary precautions to avoid causing any unwarranted damage to roads, lands, properties, trees and other features and, during the currency of the Contract, shall deal promptly with any complaints by owners or occupiers.

2. Where any portion of the Works is close to, across, or under any existing apparatus of Public Utilities or other parties, the Contractor shall temporarily support and work round, under or adjacent to all apparatus in a manner designed to avoid damage, leakage or danger, and to ensure uninterrupted operation.

(iii) The Bill of Quantities should be so prepared that Tenderers may price for working round and temporarily supporting services. Any permanent support known to be required should be described in the Contract.

3. Should any leakages or damage be discovered, the Contractor shall at once notify the Engineer and the Statutory Authority or owner concerned, and the Contractor shall afford every facility for the repair or replacement of the apparatus affected.

1.11 PUBLIC UTILITY AND OTHER SERVICES

(i) The Contract should describe any services which are known to require diverting or removing on account of their interference with the Permanent Works, or which render the construction to be unreasonably difficult.

(ii) The Water Authorities Association and British Gas have agreed a model consultative procedure for pipeline construction involving deep excavation.

(iii) 'Other services' in 1.11.1 includes connections to and from premises and services to street furniture.

(iv) The diversion or removal of Statutory Undertakers' apparatus can only be undertaken by or under the order of the appropriate Authority.

1. The positions of Public Utility and other services close to the Works are indicated in the Contract so far as they are believed to exist, but no warranty is given as to the accuracy or completeness of this information.

2. The approved programme of Works shall show information necessary to enable the Engineer to arrange for all diversions, or removals, of services described in the Contract to be carried out at the appropriate time.

3. The Contractor shall consult all relevant Statutory Authorities and service owners before commencing any excavations, and shall satisfy himself as to the exact position of existing services which may affect or be affected by the construction of the Works.

4. The Contractor shall make his own arrangements for any diversion or removal of services which he may require for his own convenience or because of his proposed method of working, and shall, in all cases, inform the Engineer in advance of his proposals.

5. Should any service be found to exist which is not indicated, or not as indicated in the Contract, the Contractor shall at once give written notification to the Engineer.

1.12 TRAFFIC REQUIREMENTS

(i) Chapter 8 covers many aspects which are sometimes found in specifications, such as traffic signals and signs, one-way working and minimum carriageway widths. See also 'Traffic Warning Signs for Roadworks', published by the Department of Transport.

(ii) Advice Note TA/6/80 defines 'minor works' and 'minor roads'.

(iii) 'Site' includes any tip provided by the Employer for the purposes of the Contract.

(iv) The Contract should include details of any road closures to be arranged by the Employer.

(v) For general requirements relating to road closures and diversions, see Paragraph 8.53 of Chapter 8.

1. The Contractor shall comply with the relevant provisions of the Traffic Safety Measures for Road Works as contained in Chapter 8 of the Traffic Signs Manual, published by Her Majesty's Stationery Office, and with the relevant provisions of Advice Notes TD/21/85: 'Portable Traffic Signals at Roadworks on Single Carriageway Roads' and TA/47/85: 'Control of Traffic at Roadworks on Single Carriageway Roads', published by the Department of Transport. Alternatively, for minor works on minor roads, signing shall comply with the relevant provisions of Advice Note TA/6/80: 'Traffic signs and safety measures for minor works on minor roads', published by the Department of Transport as an addendum to Chapter 8.

2. Before any work in or affecting the use of any highway is commenced, the Contractor's proposed method of working shall be agreed with, and confirmed in writing to, the Engineer and the Highway and Police Authorities.

3. Throughout the execution and maintenance of the Works, the Contractor shall co-operate with the Highway and Police Authorities concerning works in, or access to, the highway. The Contractor shall inform the Engineer of any requirements of, or arrangements made with, the Highway and Police Authorities.

4. Where the diversion of any existing carriageway, footway or public right of way is temporarily necessitated by the Works, the Contractor shall provide and maintain an alternative which shall be operational before interference with the existing way.

5. Where ramps are required, they shall be provided and maintained to a standard suitable in all respects for the class or classes of traffic or pedestrians requiring to use them.

6. The Contractor shall take all reasonable steps to prevent vehicles entering and leaving the Site depositing mud or other debris on the surface of adjacent roads or footways, and shall remove expeditiously any materials so deposited.

(i) See also Clauses 13(1) and 19(1) of the Fifth Edition.

1.13 TIDINESS OF SITE

1. The Contractor shall be responsible for the proper upkeep and maintenance of the Site and the Works and shall remove from the Site rubbish and other waste as it accumulates. Materials and equipment shall be positioned, stored and stacked in an orderly manner.

1.14 WORKS AFFECTING WATERCOURSES

1. The Contractor shall notify the Engineer in writing 14 days in advance of his intention to start any part of the Works affecting a watercourse, canal or lake.

2. The Contractor shall be responsible for maintaining watercourses within the Site in effective working condition at all times.

3. The Contractor shall take all practicable measures, which shall be to the prior approval of the Engineer, to prevent the deposition of silt or other material in, and the pollution of, any existing watercourse, canal, lake, reservoir, borehole, aquifer or catchment area, arising from his operations.

(i) It is assumed that all necessary Statutory consents to construct the Permanent Works will have been obtained by the Employer.

(ii) The following Statutory provisions are also relevant:

1. Impeding flow in a watercourse: Land Drainage Act 1976, section 18.

2. Pollution of a watercourse or underground strata: Control of Pollution Act 1974, sections 31, 32 and 49; Salmon & Fresh Water Fisheries Act, 1975, Section 4.

1.15 CONTAMINATION OF WATER SUPPLIES

1. Before any person is engaged on work described in the Contract as involving 'restricted operations', he shall be notified of the need for personal hygiene and the dangers of contamination, shall complete a medical questionnaire provided by the Employer and, where there is a need, shall be tested to indicate that he is not a carrier of typhoid or other waterborne disease. The Contractor shall notify the Engineer of any person who has been certified by a doctor as suffering from an illness associated with looseness of the bowels, and no such person shall be employed on such work until the Employer's medical adviser is satisfied that it is safe for him to be so employed.

2. The Contractor shall comply with the relevant provisions of 'Water Supply Hygiene – Safeguards in the Operation and Management of Public Waterworks in England and Wales', published by the National Water Council.

(i) The term 'restricted operations' is defined in Paragraph 1.03 of 'Water Supply Hygiene'.

(ii) Provision should be made in the Bill of Quantities for all medical testing required by this Clause.

(iii) The use of the term 'pathogenic organism test' has been avoided, since other tests will be involved.

1.16 CHLORINE AND SULPHUR DIOXIDE

1. Where the Contract requires the handling or use of chlorine or sulphur dioxide, or work to be carried out on, or immediately adjacent to, any existing or proposed chlorine or sulphur dioxide installation, the Contractor shall comply with the relevant provisions of 'Safe Handling of Chlorine and Sulphur Dioxide' published by the National Joint Health and Safety Committee for the Water Service.

1.17 SAFETY IN SEWERS AND AT SEWAGE WORKS

1. Where the Contract requires work to be carried out within or adjacent to any sewer or at a sewage works, the Contractor shall comply with the relevant provisions of 'Safe Working in Sewers and at Sewage Works', published by the National Joint Health and Safety Committee for the Water Service.

(i) Section 4 of 'Safe Working in Sewers and at Sewage Works' refers to the water industry guidelines for the use of respiratory protective equipment. Those guidelines should also be incorporated in any other type of contract where the use of breathing apparatus will be required.

1.18 WORK IN COMPRESSED AIR

1. Where work is to be carried out in compressed air, the Contractor shall apply to the Chief Inspector of Factories for a Certificate of Approval to the use of the decompression tables incorporated in the Medical Code of Practice for Work in Compressed Air (Third Edition) 1982, published by the Construction Industry Research and Information Association. The Contractor shall comply with all other relevant provisions of the above Code.

(i) See also The Work in Compressed Air Special Regulations 1958.

1.19 EMERGENCY ARRANGEMENTS

(i) See also Clauses 8(2) and 19(1) of the Fifth Edition.

1. The Contractor shall maintain arrangements whereby he can quickly call out labour outside normal working hours to carry out any work needed for an emergency associated with the Works. The Engineer shall be provided at all times with a list of addresses and telephone numbers of the Contractor's staff who are currently responsible for organising emergency work.

2. The Contractor shall acquaint himself and his employees with any relevant local arrangements which are in existence for dealing with emergencies.

1.20 EXPLOSIVES AND DANGEROUS SUBSTANCES

(i) The following Statutory and other provisions are also relevant:

1. Storage and Use of Explosives: The Construction (General Provisions) Regulations 1961, Part VI.
The Explosives Acts 1875 and 1923 and Orders in Council Nos. 6, 6A, 6C, 12, 13, 16 and 28 made under the 1875 Act.

2. Storage of Petroleum: The Petroleum Spirit (Motor Vehicles etc) Regulations 1929 The Petroleum (Consolidation) Act 1928

3. Storage of Highly Flammable Substances: The Highly Flammable Liquids and Liquefied Petroleum Gases Regulations 1972

1. No explosive or other dangerous substance shall be brought onto the Site or used for any purpose unless the Contractor has previously obtained the written approval of the Engineer.

2. The location of each explosives magazine and store of any other dangerous substance on the Site shall be approved in writing by the Engineer.

3. The storage of blasting explosives shall be in accordance with the relevant provisions of BS 5607.

1.21 ELECTRICITY DISTRIBUTION ON THE SITE

(i) All Area Electricity Boards require compliance with the I.E.E. Wiring Regulations where mains electricity is to be used. This Clause ensures that the same provisions apply in the case of any on-site generation.

(ii) The provisions of the I.E.E. Wiring Regulations embrace BS 4363 (Distribution Units for Electricity Supplies for Construction and Building Sites) and CP 1017 (Distribution of Electricity on Construction and Building Sites).

1. All electrical installations forming part of the Temporary Works shall comply with the relevant provisions of the 'Regulations for Electrical Installations' (I.E.E. Wiring Regulations – 15th Edition), published by the Institution of Electrical Engineers.

1.22 BRITISH STANDARDS AND OTHER DOCUMENTS

(i) The period of 42 days is consistent with that used for defining the 'Base Index Figure' in sub-clause (2)(b) of the Contract Price Fluctuations clause for use in connection with the Fifth Edition.

1. British Standards and other documents referred to in the Contract shall be deemed to be those current 42 days prior to the date for return of Tenders.

2. Any reference in the Contract to a Standard published by the British Standards Institution, or to the specification of another body, shall be construed equally as reference to an equivalent one.

ASSOCIATED TOPICS

The following topics are dealt with by statute or by the Fifth Edition of the ICE Conditions of Contract and are therefore excluded from the Specification:

1. NOISE:

Clause 29(2) of the Fifth Edition deals with the subject generally, but special clauses may be necessary depending on particular circumstances. The provisions of Part III of the Control of Pollution Act 1974 and the Health and Safety at Work etc. Act 1974 will apply. Statutory Instrument S.I. 1992/84, made under the Control of Pollution Act 1974, gave approval to the use of BS 5228 (Noise Control on Construction and Demolition Sites) in relation to the control of construction noise.

2. CARE AND PROTECTION OF THE WORKS:

See Clauses 20(1) and 39(1) of the Fifth Edition.

3. ILLUMINATION OF WORKS:

See Regulation 47 of the Construction (General Provisions) Regulations 1961.

4. WATCHING AND LIGHTING:

See Clause 19(1) of the Fifth Edition and Part 5 of the Chapter 8 of the Traffic Signs Manual.

5. FIRST AID:

See the Health and Safety (First-Aid) Regulations 1981.

6. SITE ROADS:
See Clause 8(1) of the Fifth Edition.

7. ACCESS LADDERS, PLATFORMS ETC:

See The Construction (Working Places) Regulations 1966.

8. WELFARE FACILITIES:

See The Construction (Health and Welfare) Regulations 1966 as amended by The Construction (Health and Welfare) (Amended) Regulations 1974, and section 7 of the Factories Act 1961.

9. SITE INVESTIGATION:

See the following:

(i) Clause 11(1) of the Fifth Edition.

(ii) BS 5930 and CIRIA Special Publication 25 – 'Site investigation manual'

(iii) Clause 3.3 of 'Guidance on the Preparation, Submission and Consideration of Tenders for Civil Engineering Contracts' recommended for use in the United Kingdom and produced by the ICE Conditions of Contract Standing Joint Committee.

10. CONTRACTORS' SITE ACCOMMODATION:

(i) For the provision and adequacy of the Contractor's accommodations see Clauses 8(1) and 11(1) of the Fifth Edition.

(ii) For the Contractor's responsibilities for obtaining any planning permissions which may be required in respect of his accommodations see Clause 26(2) of the Fifth Edition.

11. CONFIDENTIALITY:

Any requirement for the Contractor to treat the Contract or any part of it as private and confidential should be a Special Condition of Contract and not a Specification clause.

12. FIRE PRECAUTIONS IN SITE ACCOMMODATIONS:

For requirements as to fire certificates for site accommodations, see Paragraph 15 of Part 1 of Schedule 1 to the Fire Certificates (Special Premises) Regulations 1976.

13. NUISANCE:

See Clause 29 of the Fifth Edition and section 92 of the Public Health Act 1936.

14. DEALING WITH FLOWS IN SEWERS:

See Clauses 8(1) and 14(3) of the Fifth Edition. Estimates of dry-weather and peak flows should be indicated in the Contract.

15. WATER INDUSTRY'S DUTY TO CONTRACTORS:

See 'The Water Industry's Duty under the Health and Safety at Work etc. Act to Contractors Employed by the Industry', published by the National Joint Health and Safety Committee Employers' Side as an Employers' only guideline.

SECTION 2

MATERIALS

2.1 STANDARDS AND SUBMISSION OF MATERIALS

1. Wherever, in respect of any British Standard (BS), a BSI Kitemark Certification Scheme is available, all materials required to comply with that Standard, or the containers of such materials, shall be marked with the BSI Certification Trade Mark (the Kitemark). The mark of confirmity of any other third party certification body accredited by the National Accreditation Council for Certification Bodies or equivalent shall be an acceptable alternative to this requirement.

2. Wherever, in respect of any Water Industry specification (WIs) published by the WAA Sewers and Water Mains Committee or its predecessor, a Water Industry Certification Scheme or equivalent is available, all materials required to comply with that specification, or the containers of such materials, shall be marked with the Water Industry Certification Mark (the Watermark) or the mark of conformity of the equivalent scheme.

3. The requirements of sub-clauses 1 and 2 above shall not apply where the Engineer is satisfied and confirms to the Contractor in writing that third party quality assured materials are not readily available. In such a case, and where materials are required to comply with other British Standards, specifications or their equivalents, the Contractor shall submit to the Engineer test certificates, furnished by the supplier or manufacturer of the materials, indicating compliance with the relevant specification.

4. As soon as possible after the Contract has been awarded, the Contractor shall submit to the Engineer for his approval a list of his proposed suppliers and sources of materials required for the execution of the Works.

5. Samples shall be taken in accordance with the appropriate British Standard where applicable.

6. The materials subsequently supplied shall conform to the quality of samples which have been approved by the Engineer.

7. Names of additional suppliers and sources may be submitted by the Contractor during the execution of the Contract, but no source of supply shall be changed without the Engineer's approval.

(i) Where appropriate, additional quality control of materials should be carried out at manufacturers' or suppliers' premises.

(ii) In January 1989 the WAA Sewers and Water Mains Committee announced that all specifications produced in its Information and Guidance Note series were to be known henceforth as Water Industry specifications (WIs). The numbering system remains unchanged.

(iii) For the Engineer's right of access to suppliers' premises, see Clause 37 of the Fifth Edition.

(iv) For the terms under which samples are to be supplied, see Clause 36(2) of the Fifth Edition. For testing, see Additional description rule A3 to Class 'A' of the CESMM.

(v) Where the Contract requires the use of a material which will come into contact with potable water, or water to be used for potable supply, reference should be made to the current issue of the Water Fittings and Materials Directory, published by the Water Research Centre and to the current Statement of the Committee on Chemicals and Materials of Construction for Use in Public Water Supply and Swimming Pools, issued by the Department of the Environment. Where appropriate, copies of each list should be made available to Tenderers.

(vi) BS 6920 and IGN No. 5-01-03 deal respectively with requirements for the testing of non-metallic and metallic materials for use in contact with potable water.

2.2 STORAGE OF MATERIALS

1. Materials and components shall be stored in such a manner as to preserve their quality and condition to the standards required by the Contract.

2. The quantity of materials and components stored on the Site shall be consistent with that necessary for efficient working.

2.3 HANDLING AND USE OF MATERIALS

1. Materials and components shall be handled in such a manner as to avoid any damage or contamination, and in accordance with all applicable recommendations of the manufacturers.

(i) An understanding of manufacturers' recommendations is necessary before their suitability can be assessed.

2. Unless otherwise described in the Contract, the use, installation, application or fixing of materials and components shall be in accordance with all applicable recommendations of the manufacturers. Where appropriate, the Contractor shall make use of any technical advisory services offered by manufacturers.

(i) For the definition of in-situ topsoil, see Clause 3.3.

(i) For in-situ turf for relaying, see Clauses 3.2 and 3.9.

(ii) Clause 3a of BS 3969 permits up to 40% of Dwarf Leafy Perennial Ryegrass unless otherwise specified.

(i) The four mixtures given are available nationally, examples of their individual application being as follows:

Mixture	Application
1	General application which will give satisfactory germination on a wide variety of soils.
2	Heavy soils and wet areas.
3	Drier, less fertile soils.
4	Soils with very low fertility, low pH or sandy soils.

(ii) All mixtures have been selected to provide slow growing grass with a low maintenance requirement. Mixture 1 will give the most rapid cover after germination, but will require more maintenance than Mixtures 2, 3 and 4.

(iii) The mixtures are not intended for use on agricultural land, where the farmer's requirements should be ascertained.

(iv) The required grass seed mixture should be described in the Contract.

(v) For guidance on the use of grass in hydraulic engineering practice, see CIRIA Technical Note 71.

(vi) In view of the duties on water authorities under the Wildlife and Countryside Act 1981, consideration should be given where appropriate to the inclusion of an approved wild flower mix with the grass seed.

2.4 IMPORTED TOPSOIL

1. Imported topsoil shall comply with BS 3882 and be of light or medium texture, having a pH value of between 6.0 and 7.5 . Imported topsoil shall not contain stones greater than 50 mm in size, nor have a total stone content exceeding 10% by mass.

2.5 IMPORTED TURF

1. Imported turf shall comply with BS 3969 and be delivered to the Site within 36 hours of lifting. Constituent grasses and their proportions shall comply with the provisions of Clause 3a of BS 3969.

2. Turves shall be 300 mm wide and of uniform thickness not less than 40 mm, in lengths not exceeding 1 m. Turves shall not be lifted in frosty weather.

2.6 GRASS SEED

1. Grass seed shall be a tested blend of named varieties and certificates of purity and germination shall be provided. The blend shall consist of one of the following mixtures:

Variety	Percentage by mass			
	Mixture 1	Mixture 2	Mixture 3	Mixture 4
Dwarf Leafy Perennial Ryegrass	20–30	–	–	–
Smooth-stalked Meadow Grass	25–35	–	20–30	0–15
Rough-stalked Meadow Grass	–	15–25	–	–
Creeping Red Fescue	30–40	40–50	35–45	20–50
Fine Leaved Sheep's Fescue	–	–	10–20	10–40
Chewings Fescue	–	–	–	10–40
Browntop Bent	5–15	5–15	5–15	0–10
Crested Dogstail	–	–	5–15	–
Timothy	–	20–30	–	–
White Clover	–	–	–	0–10

2.7 FERTILIZER

1. Fertilizers shall consist of compounds containing urea nitrogen, phosphoric acid and potash in the proportions by mass, as set out below:

Chemical	General purpose	Pre-seeding	Post-establishment
Urea nitrogen	5%	–	46%
Phosphoric acid	15%	21%	–
Potash	15%	12%	–

(i) The general purpose compound should be used as a single application, prior to seeding, where good root establishment but slow growth is required. The pre-seeding and post-establishment compounds require application both before and after germination respectively and will promote good root establishment, followed by rapid growth.

(ii) The compounds are not intended for use on agricultural land, where the farmer's requirements should be ascertained.

2.8 TREES AND SHRUBS

1. Trees and shrubs shall comply with the relevant provisions of the appropriate British Standard, as set out below:

Type	BS
Ordinary nursery stock	3936: Part1
Semi-mature trees	4043
Advanced nursery stock	5236

2.9 WATER

1. Water for use with cement, or in contact with potable water mains and installations, shall be obtained from a public utility undertaking supply and be of potable quality.

(i) In certain areas, supplementary mains carrying non-potable water have been laid, and the use of this water with cement or in contact with potable water mains and installations has been prohibited.

(ii) Where potable mains water is not available, alternative provisions should be described in the Contract. BS 3148 gives details of tests for water for making concrete.

2.10 AGGREGATES FOR CONCRETE

1. Aggregates for concrete shall comply with the relevant provisions of the appropriate British Standard, as set out below:

Type of aggregate	Type of concrete	
	Ordinary prescribed mixes and those designed to retain an aqueous liquid	Designed mixes and special prescribed mixes
Aggregates from natural sources	BS 882	BS 882
Air-cooled blastfurnace slag aggregate	BS 1047	BS 1047
Foamed or expanded blastfurnace slag lightweight aggregate	–	BS 877: Part 2
Clinker and furnace bottom ash aggregates	–	BS 1165
Lightweight aggregates	–	BS 3797: Part 2

(i) Any restrictions on the source, type or group classification of aggregates should be described in the Contract.

(ii) Concrete designed to retain an aqueous liquid should be described as such in the Contract.

(iii) Where there is the likelihood of unacceptable damage from alkali-silica reaction, specific precautions to minimise it should be described in the Contract in accordance with the recommendations of Technical Report No. 30 ('Alkali-silica Reaction – Minimising the Risk of Damage to Concrete') published by the Concrete Society in October 1987 and BRE Digest 330 published by the Building Research Establishment in March 1988.

(iv) For the limitation of total chloride ion content of the concrete mix, see Clause 4.8.2.

(v) The limit for water absorption is consistent with Clause 6.2.2 of BS 8007.

2. Aggregates complying with BS 877: Part 2, BS 1047, BS 1165 or BS 3797: Part 2 shall have values of 'ten per cent fines', aggregate impact and chloride ion content which are consistent with the relevant provisions of BS 882.

3. The water absorption of aggregates for concrete designed to retain an aqueous liquid shall not exceed 3% when measured in accordance with BS 812: Part 2.

2.11 AGGREGATES FOR HIGH STRENGTH CONCRETE TOPPING
1. Aggregates for high strength concrete topping (granolithic finish) shall comply with BS 882 and be 10 mm nominal size, graded in accordance with Table 6 of that Standard.

2.12 SANDS
1. Sands for mortar and grout shall comply with BS 1200 and be graded in accordance with Table 1 of that Standard.

(i) The requirement for sands to be washed is additional to the requirements of the Standards, but is in line with the main conclusion of CIRIA Report 59 – 'Building Sands: Availability, Usage and Compliance with Specification Requirements'.

2. Sands for floor screeds shall comply with the relevant provisions of BS 882.

3. Sands for external renderings and internal plastering with lime and Portland cement shall comply with the relevant provisions of BS 1199.

4. All sands required to comply with BS 882, BS 1199 or BS 1200 shall be washed sands.

2.13 GROUND GRANULATED BLASTFURNACE SLAG
1. Ground granulated blastfurnace slag (ggbs) for use with Portland cement shall comply with BS 6699.

2.14 PULVERIZED-FUEL ASH
1. Pulverized-fuel ash (pfa) for use as a component material in cementitious grout or non-structural concrete shall comply with BS 3892: Part 2, Grade A.

2. Pfa for use as a cementitious component in structural concrete and annulus grouts shall comply with BS 3892: Part 1. Pfa for annulus grouts shall be preblended and bagged before delivery to the Site.

3. Conditioned pfa for use as a fill material shall be supplied with an optimum moisture content and maximum dry density in the ranges 18–25% and 1200–1500 kg/m^3 respectively, when determined in accordance with Test 12 of BS 1377. Water content shall be within $\pm 2\%$ of the optimum moisture content.

2.15 CEMENT
1. Cement shall:

(i) The permitted type(s) of cement should be described in the Contract.

(ii) The Third Division of Class 'F' of the CESMM requires that the type of cement should be stated in item descriptions for in-situ concrete. The remaining work classifications are not so specific, and, to ensure clarity, the required type of cement should always be stated.

(iii) BS 5224 and BS 6610 cements are not 'permitted cements' under BS 5328, nor are they included in BS 8110: Part 1.

(iv) BS 146: Part 2 permits the 'cement' to contain not more than 65% ggbs by mass.

(a) be factory-produced by the cement manufacturer and comply with the provisions of the appropriate British Standard, as set out below:

Cement type	BS
Ordinary Portland	12
Rapid hardening Portland	12
Portland – blastfurnace	146: Part 2
Low-heat Portland	1370
Sulphate-resisting Portland	4027
Low-heat Portland – blastfurnace	4246: Part 2
Supersulphated	4248
Masonry	5224
Pozzolanic cement with pfa as pozzolana	6610
Portland pfa	6588

(v) Special combinations of cement facilitate additional resistance to sulphate attack. See Table 6.1 of BS 8110: Part 1.

(vi) Where there is the likelihood of unacceptable damage from alkali-silica reaction, specific precautions to minimise it should be described in the Contract in accordance with the recommendations of Technical Report No. 30 ('Alkali-silica Reaction – Minimising the Risk of Damage to Concrete') published by the Concrete Society in October 1987 and BRE Digest 330 published by the Building Research Establishment in March 1988.

(vii) Cement for annulus grouts should comply with either BS 12 or BS 4027.

or

(b) consist of a normal or special combination of cement complying with the relevant provisions of BS 12 and ggbs or pfa in accordance with the following, to be included as part of the concrete mix by simultaneously combining them with the other concrete materials at the concrete mixer:

Cementitious component other than cement	Use of concrete	British Standard to be complied with	Percentage by mass of total cementitious content	
			normal	special
pfa	Any	BS 3892: Part 1	15 – 35	25 – 40
ggbs	Concrete designed to retain an aqueous liquid	BS 6699	0 – 50	70 – 90
ggbs	Other	BS 6699	0 – 65	70 – 90

2. For all cement used in structural concrete the Contractor shall provide when requested by the Engineer certificates of the relevant proportions of any ggbs or pfa.

3. White and coloured Portland cement shall comply with the chemical and physical requirements of BS 12. Added pigments shall comply with BS 1014 and shall be mixed with the cement in accordance with the manufacturer's instructions. The amount of added pigments shall not exceed 10% of cement by mass, except for carbon black, where the limit shall be 2%.

2.16 ADMIXTURES FOR CONCRETE OR GROUT

(i) Clause 4 of BS 5328 prohibits the use of admixtures in ordinary prescribed mixes.

(ii) Clause 2.16.2 is consistent with Clause 6.1.5.4 of BS 8110: Part 1.

1. Accelerating, retarding and water-reducing admixtures for concrete or grout shall comply with the relevant provisions in BS 5075: Part 1. Air-entraining admixtures shall comply with the relevant provisions of BS 5075: Part 2. Superplasticizing admixtures shall comply with the relevant provisions of BS 5075: Part 3.

2. Calcium chloride shall not be used in concrete which is to be reinforced, contain embedded metal, or has been designed to retain an aqueous liquid. Where used with sulphate-resisting cement, or in concrete which is to be reinforced or contain embedded metal, the chloride ion content of admixtures shall not exceed 2% by mass of the admixture or 0.03% by mass of the cement. Admixtures containing chlorides shall not be used in reinforced concrete designed to retain an aqueous liquid.

2.17 LIME FOR MORTAR

(i) Clause 23.2.3 of BS 5628: Part 3 advises that lime used for mortar should be non-hydraulic (high calcium or magnesian) or semi-hydraulic (i.e. lime putty).

1. Lime for mortar shall be in the form of lime putty, complying with the relevant provisions of BS 890.

2.18 FILTER MEDIA

(i) The nominal size of medium should be described in the Contract.

(ii) Appendix E6 of BS 1438 gives recommendations for the placing of filter media.

(iii) An additional specification will be required for a filter medium other than those covered by BS 1438.

1. Media from natural sources, or which derives from the reduction of iron ore in a blastfurnace, and for use as medium in biological percolating filters, shall be crushed stone, gravel or blastfurnace slag complying with the relevant provisions of BS 1438.

2.19 CEMENT GROUTS

(i) The required class of grout, together with the type of cement and any admixture, should be described in the Contract.

1. Cement grout shall be mixed in the relevant proportions indicated in the following table using the minimum quantity of water to ensure the necessary fluidity and to render it capable of penetrating the work.

Class	Nominal mix by mass		
	Cement	Sand	pfa
G1	1	–	–
G2	1	3	–
G3	1	10	–
G4	1	–	10
G5	1	–	4
G6	1	–	½

2. Cement grout shall be used within one hour of mixing, except where containing a retardant admixture.

3. Sulphate-resisting cement shall not be used as a constituent of grouts containing pfa.

2.20 MORTAR

(i) Although the CESMM generally requires components of concrete and grout mixes to be measured by mass, there is no corresponding reference to mortars. Volumetric mixes consistent with BS 5628: Part 3, BS 4721 and PD 6472 have, therefore, been specified.

(ii) IGN No. 4-10-01 deals with mortar.

1. Mortar shall be mixed only as and when required in the relevant proportions indicated in the following table, until its colour and consistency are uniform. The constituent materials shall be accurately gauged, allowance being made for bulking of sand.

Nominal mix by volume				
Class	Cement:lime putty:sand	Cement:sand with plasticizer	Class	Masonry cement: sand
M1	1:0 to ¼:3	1:2½ to 3	M5	1:2 to 2½
M2	1:½:4 to 4½	1:3 to 4	M6	1:2½ to 3½
M3	1:1:5 to 6	1:5 to 6	M7	1:4 to 5
M4	1:2:8 to 9	1:7 to 8	M8	1:5½ to 6½

2. Ready-mixed lime: sand for mortar and ready-to-use retarded mortar shall comply with the relevant provisions of BS 4721.

3. All mortar shall be conveyed fresh to the Works as required for use. Mortar which has begun to set or which has been Site-mixed for a period of more than one hour in the case of classes M1, M2, M5 and M6, and two hours in the case of Classes M3, M4, M7 and M8 shall not be used. Plasticizing and set retarding mortar admixtures shall comply with BS 4887: Parts 1 and 2 respectively and shall be supplied with instructions for use.

2.21 STEEL REINFORCEMENT

(i) The Contract should describe whether Type 1 (square twisted) or Type 2 (ribbed) high yield steel bars are required.

1. Steel reinforcement shall comply with the relevant provisions of the appropriate British Standard, as set out below:

Type	BS
Carbon steel bars	4449
Cold reduced steel wire	4482
Steel fabric	4483

2. Steel fabric reinforcement shall be welded at the intersections and, unless otherwise described in the Contract, shall be delivered to the Site in flat sheets.

2.22 TYING WIRE

1. Tying wire for steel reinforcement shall be 1.6 mm diameter finally annealed mild steel wire, complying with BS 1052.

2.23 COVER BLOCKS AND SPACERS FOR REINFORCEMENT

1. Cover blocks and spacers shall be designed to maintain the correct clear cover of concrete over steel reinforcement, shall be as small as possible consistent with their purpose, and of a shape acceptable to the Engineer.

2. Concrete cover blocks shall be manufactured with a 10 mm maximum aggregate size and otherwise produced to the same specification as the surrounding concrete. Wire cast in the block for the purpose of tying it to the reinforcement shall comply with Clause 2.22.

3. Spacers shall be of rust-proof material and shall not produce staining, or otherwise be detrimental to the concrete or steel.

2.24 PRECAST CONCRETE PRODUCTS

1. Constituent materials of precast concrete products shall comply with the relevant requirements of this Specification, except where an appropriate British Standard includes specified requirements to the contrary.

2. Except where otherwise specified in a relevant British Standard or described in the Contract, the surface finish of precast concrete products shall be Rough Finish for surfaces next to earth and elsewhere Fair Finish.

2.25 WATERPROOF PAPER

1. Waterproof paper shall be Grade 'BIF' complying with the relevant provisions of BS 1521.

2.26 PLASTIC SHEETING AND SLEEVING

(i) A film thickness of 125 μm is equivalent to 500 gauge.

1. Plastic sheeting for waterproof underlay shall be free from tears and voids and be substantially free from pinholes and other discontinuities. It shall have a composition in accordance with Clause 3 of BS 6076 and a nominal film thickness of 125 μm.

(ii) The colour specifications and amended requirements for layflat widths are consistent with the recommendations of IGN No. 4-50-01.

(iii) IGN No. 4-50-02 gives operational guidelines for the transportation, handling and laying of ductile iron pipes with factory applied polyethylene sleeving.

2. Tubular polyethylene film for use as a loose protective sleeving for buried iron pipes and fittings shall comply with the relevant provisions of BS 6076, except that the nominal layflat width shall be 280 mm for use with 80 mm and 100 mm nominal internal diameter pipelines incorporating push-in flexible joints, and 400 mm for 150 mm nominal internal diameter pipelines. Sleeving for pipes for below ground use for potable water shall be coloured blue and all other sleeving black.

2.27 VITRIFIED CLAY PIPES AND PIPELINE FITTINGS

(i) IGN No. 4-11-01 deals with vitrified clay pipes and fittings.

1. Vitrified clay pipes and pipeline fittings shall comply with the relevant provisions of BS 65 and be of 'normal' Type with flexible mechanical joints, unless otherwise described in the Contract.

(ii) The type of joint and jointing materials for extra chemically resistant pipes should be described in the Contract.

2. Extra chemically resistant pipes and fittings shall comply with the relevant provisions of BS 65.

2.28 CONCRETE PIPES AND FITTINGS

(i) Particular requirements from the options listed in Appendix A of BS 5911: Parts 100 or 120, or Appendix A2 of BS 5911: Part 3, should be described in the Contract.

1. Unreinforced and reinforced concrete pipes and fittings with flexible or ogee joints shall comply with the relevant provisions of BS 5911: Parts 100 and 3 respectively.

2. All pipes and fittings shall have gasket-type joints of spigot and socket or rebated form, unless otherwise described in the Contract.

(ii) Sub-clause 3 expressly provides for the Contractor to be responsible for the adequacy of the design of pipes for jacking insofar as it is relevant to his operations. See Clause 8(2) of the Fifth Edition.

(iii) IGN No. 4-12-01 deals with unreinforced and reinforced concrete pipes.

3. Concrete jacking pipes shall comply with the relevant provisions of BS 5911: Part 120. Additionally, the Contractor shall ensure that the pipes can withstand the jacking loads to which they will be subjected during installation, without cracking or spalling. A certificate shall be supplied, confirming that the pipes are suitable for jacking and stating the distributed jacking loads for which they were designed.

(i) IGN No. 4-12-02 deals with glass composite concrete pipes.

(ii) Particular requirements from the options listed in Appendix A of BS 5911: Part 101 should be described in the Contract.

2.29 GLASS COMPOSITE CONCRETE (GCC) PIPES

1. Glass composite concrete (gcc) pipes and fittings with flexible joints shall comply with the relevant provisions of BS 5911: Part 101.

(i) Particular requirements from the options listed in Appendix C of BS 4625 or Appendix A of BS 5178 should be described in the Contract.

(ii) The Contract should describe whether cylinder or non-cylinder type pipes and fittings are required.

2.30 PRESTRESSED CONCRETE PIPES AND FITTINGS

1. Prestressed concrete pressure pipes and fittings shall comply with the relevant provisions of BS 4625. Prestressed concrete pipes and fittings for drainage and sewerage purposes shall comply with the relevant provisions of BS 5178.

2. Unless steam cured, no pipes or fittings shall leave the place of manufacture until they have been allowed to cure and mature under suitable conditions for a total period of not less than 28 days. The surface finish shall be assessed in accordance and comply with the provisions of Clause 7.5 of BS 5911: Part 100.

(i) IGN No. 4-21-01 deals with ductile iron pipes and fittings.

(ii) IGN No. 4-51-01 deals with external zinc coating of ductile iron pipe, which BS 4772 now requires on all pipes in the diameter range 80 – 800 mm.

2.31 DUCTILE IRON PIPES AND FITTINGS

1. Ductile iron pipes, fittings and joints shall comply with the relevant provisions of BS 4772.

(i) IGN No. 4-31-01 deals with unplasticized PVC pipes and fittings.

(ii) The colour and size limitation for uPVC pressure pipes are consistent with the current recommendations of the National Joint Utilities Group.

2.32 UNPLASTICIZED PVC PIPES AND FITTINGS

1. Unplasticized PVC pressure pipes shall comply with the relevant provisions of BS 3505. Pipes for below ground use for potable water and having an outside diameter less than 75 mm shall be coloured blue.

2. Joints and fittings for pressure pipes in accordance with BS 3505 shall comply with the relevant provisions of BS 4346: Parts 1 and 2 for solvent welded and mechanical joints respectively.

3. Unplasticized PVC pipes, joints and fittings for gravity sewers and drains shall comply with the relevant provisions of BS 4660 or BS 5481.

4. Solid wall concentric external rib-reinforced unplasticized PVC sewer pipe shall comply with the relevant provisions of WIs No. 4-31-05.

5. Solvent cements for jointing unplasticized PVC pipes shall comply with BS 4346: Part 3. For pipes and fittings complying with BS 4660, solvent cement may alternatively comply with BS 6209.

(i) IGN No. 4-12-03 deals with asbestos-cement pipes and fittings.

2.33 ASBESTOS-CEMENT PIPES AND FITTINGS

1. Asbestos-cement pipes, joints and fittings for sewers shall comply with the relevant provisions for BS 3656.

2. Asbestos-cement pressure pipes, joints and bends shall comply with the relevant provisions of BS 486.

(i) IGN No. 4-34-01 deals with GRP pipes and fittings.

2.34 GLASS FIBRE REINFORCED PLASTICS (GRP) PIPES AND FITTINGS

1. Glass fibre reinforced plastics (grp) pipes and fittings shall comply with the relevant provisions of BS 5480: Parts 1 and 2.

2.35 ACRYLONITRILE-BUTADIENE-STYRENE (ABS) PIPES AND FITTINGS

1. Acrylonitrile-butadiene-styrene (abs) pressure pipes and fittings shall comply with the relevant provisions of BS 5391: Part 1 and BS 5392: Part 1 respectively.

2.36 POLYETHYLENE PIPES

(i) The water industry's policy is that polyethylene pipe used for underground water supply purposes should be coloured blue.

(ii) BS 6730 deals with black poly-ethylene pipe for unprotected above ground use.

1. Blue polyethylene pipe up to nominal size 63 for below ground use for potable water shall comply with the relevant provisions of BS 6572.

2. Polyethylene pressure pipes for below ground use for cold potable water in nominal sizes greater than 63 shall comply with the relevant provisions of WIs No. 4-32-03, except that for sewage rising mains the colour shall be black.

3. Polyethylene fusion joints and fittings for use with cold potable water shall comply with the relevant provisions of WIs No. 4-32-04.

2.37 PROPYLENE COPOLYMER PRESSURE PIPES

1. Propylene copolymer pressure pipe shall comply with the relevant provisions of BS 4991 and, where to be in contact with potable water, shall be Series 1.

2.38 RAINWATER PIPES AND GUTTERS

(i) The Contract should describe the section required for asbestos-cement, aluminium and uPVC gutters.

(ii) The Contract should describe the required grade and shape of sheet and strip aluminium pipes and gutters.

(iii) BS 6087 deals with flexible joints for cast iron drainpipes and fittings.

(iv) The Contract should describe whether ears are required on cast iron pipes and fittings.

(v) The Contract should describe the required colour of uPVC pipes and fittings.

1. Rainwater pipes, gutters, fixings and accessories shall comply with the relevant provisions of the appropriate British Standard, as set out below:

Material	BS
Cast iron	460, Type A
Asbestos-cement	569
Aluminium	2997
uPVC	4576: Part 1

2.39 SOIL, WASTE AND VENTILATING PIPES

(i) BS 6087 deals with flexible joints for cast iron soil, waste and ventilating pipes and fittings.

1. Soil, waste and ventilating pipes, fittings and accessories for above-ground drainage systems shall comply with the relevant provisions of the appropriate British Standard, as set out below:

Material	BS
Cast iron	416, Type A
uPVC (soil and ventilating)	4514
Polypropylene (waste)	5254
Plastics (waste)	5255

2. Wash basin and sink wastes shall comply with the relevant provisions of BS 3380.

3. Plastics waste traps shall comply with the relevant provisions of BS 3943.

2.40 WATER FITTINGS

(i) Water Supply Byelaws are relevant to water fittings used in connection with the supply and use of water.

(ii) The required class of plastics service pipes, pump delivery pipes and distributing pipes and fittings should be described in the Contract. Where copper is to be used, the required designation and condition should be described.

1. Water fittings shall comply with the relevant provisions of the appropriate specification, as set out below:

(iii) IGN No. 5-01-01 deals with the United Kingdom Water Fittings Byelaws Scheme.

Water fitting	Type/Material	BS/WIs No.
Service pipes, pump delivery pipes, distributing pipes and fittings	Copper	2871: Part 1
	Capillary and compression fittings for copper tubes	864: Part 2
	Polyethylene	6572
	Copper and copper alloy compression fittings for polyethylene pipes	WIs No. 4-22-01
	Joints and fittings for polyethylene pipes (performance)	5114
	uPVC	3505
	uPVC joints and fittings (solvent welded)	4346: Part 1
	uPVC joints and fittings (mechanical)	4346: Part 2
Draining taps	Screw-down pattern	2879
Draw-off taps	Metal bodied (performance)	5412: Parts 1 – 5
	Plastics bodied (performance)	5413: Parts 1 – 5
Stopvalves	Above-ground, screw-down pattern	1010: Part 2
	Underground	5433
Float operated valves	Diaphgram type (brass body)	1212: Part 2
	Diaphragm type (plastics body)	1212: Part 3
Floats for ballvalves	Copper	1968
	Plastics	2456
Storage cisterns and lids	Low carbon steel	417: Part 2
	Polyolefin or olefin copolymer	4213
Wash basins	Ceramic	1188
	Metal hand rinse	1329
Sinks	Glazed fireclay	1206
	Stainless steel	1244: Part 2
WC pans	Horizontal outlet	5503: Parts 1 & 2
Connectors for WC pans	Plastics	5627
WC seats and covers	Plastics, Type 1	1254
WC flushing cisterns	Dual flush type	1125
Urinals	Stainless steel slab	4880: Part 1
	Vitreous china bowl	5520
Automatic flushing cisterns for urinals	Lidded	1876

2.41   PTFE TAPE

1.   Unsintered polytetrafluoroethylene (PTFE) tape for thread sealing applications shall comply with BS 4375.

2.42   MARKER TAPE

1. Marker tape for buried water mains shall be blue PVC or polyethylene mesh or ribbon at least 50 mm wide, incorporating a corrosion resistant tracing system.

2. Marker tape for buried cables shall be yellow PVC or polyethylene mesh or ribbon at least 150 mm wide. Ribbon shall be printed with the words 'ELECTRIC CABLE' in bold capital letters at intervals not exceeding 700 mm.

2.43 PIPES FOR LAND DRAINAGE AND TEMPORARY DRAINS

1. Pipes, joints and fittings for land drainage and temporary drains shall comply with the relevant provisions of the appropriate British Standard, as set out below:

Type	BS
'Perforated' or 'Surface water' vitrified clay pipes and fittings	65
Concrete porous pipes for under drainage	1194
Clayware field drain pipes	1196
Plastics pipes for use as light duty sub-soil drains	4962
'Land drainage' category concrete pipes and fittings with ogee joints	5911: Part 3

2.44 PIPES FOR DUCTS

(i) CP 413 gives guidance on ducts for building services.

(ii) Certain Public Utilities may require ducts to be of a particular colour. See also BS 1710.

1. Pipes, joints and fittings for exposed ducts for building services shall comply with the relevant provisions of the appropriate British Standard, as set out below:

Type	BS
Unplasticized PVC pipe	3505 or 3506
Hollow steel sections (greater than 150 mm OD)	4360, 43C to 4848: Part 2
Steel tubes (not greater than 150 mm OD)	6323: Part 2, HFW 2

2. Pipes, joints and fittings for buried ducts shall have flexible mechanical joints and comply with the relevant provisions of the appropriate British Standard, as set out below:

Type	BS
Vitrified clay	65
Asbestos-cement	3656
Unreinforced or reinforced concrete	5911: Part 100
Unplasticized PVC	4660 or 5481

2.45 DRAW CORD

1. Draw cord for duct threading shall be 8 mm diameter 3-strand hawser laid polypropylene rope complying with BS 4928.

2.46 JOINT RINGS AND LUBRICANTS

(i) IGN No. 4-40-01 deals with the selection, properties, storage and installation requirements for elastomeric seals and sealing rings.

1. Rubber joint rings for water mains and drainage purposes shall be Types W and D respectively, complying with the relevant provisions of BS 2494, and shall be obtained from the pipe manufacturer.

2. Joint lubricants for sliding joints shall have no deleterious effects on either the joint rings or pipes, and be unaffected by the liquid to be conveyed. Lubricants to be used for jointing water mains shall not impart to water taste, colour, or any effect known to be injurious to health, and shall be resistant to bacterial growth.

2.47 FLANGES FOR PIPES AND PIPELINE FITTINGS

1. Flanges for pipes and pipeline fittings shall, unless otherwise required by the Contract, comply with BS 4504: Part 1 for 16 bar nominal pressure rating.

(i) The general use of a 16 bar nominal pressure rating is consistent with the recommendation of the Sewers and Water Mains Committee.

(ii) Flanges in accordance with BS 4772 are dimensionally compatible with BS 4504: Part 1.

2.48 GASKETS FOR FLANGED JOINTS

1. Gaskets for flanged pipe joints shall be of the inside-bolt-circle type. The dimensions of gaskets shall comply with BS 4865: Part 1. Gaskets shall be manufactured from material complying with the provisions of BS 2494 for Type W rings.

(i) Any requirement for full face gaskets should be described in the Contract.

2.49 VALVES

1. Valves for pipeline installation shall comply with the relevant provisions of the appropriate British Standard, as set out below:

Type	BS
Cast iron wedge and double disk gate valves	5150
Cast iron gate (parallel slide) valves	5151
Cast iron check valves	5153
Copper alloy globe, globe stop and check, check and gate valves	5154
Butterfly valves	5155
Diaphragm valves	5156
Cast iron and carbon steel plug valves	5158
Predominantly key-operated cast iron gate valves for waterworks purposes	5163

(i) Particular requirements from the options listed in the various Standards should be described in the Contract.

(ii) BS 6683 deals with the installation and use of valves.

(iii) IGN No. 4-23-01 deals with the selection, installation, operation and maintenance of isolating and boundary valves used in water distribution systems.

2. Valve parts to be in contact with potable water shall meet the relevant provisions of BS 6920: Part 1 or IGN No. 5-01-03 as appropriate.

2.50 PIPE BEDDING AND SIDEFILL MATERIALS

1. Imported granular and selected 'as-dug bedding and sidefill Type A' materials for buried pipelines shall comply with the recommendations of WIs No. 4-08-01.

2. Sand for bedding pipes shall comply with the provisions of BS 882, Table 5 for Grading Zone C.

3. Selected main backfill Type B, whether selected from locally excavated material or imported, shall consist of uniform readily compactible material, free from vegetable matter, building rubbish and frozen material, or materials susceptible to spontaneous combustion, and excluding clay of liquid limit greater than 80 and/or plastic limit greater than 55 and materials of excessively high moisture content. Clay lumps and stones retained on 75 mm and 37.5 mm sieves respectively shall be excluded from the fill material.

(i) The Contract should describe the size and type of aggregate required.

2.51 PRECAST CONCRETE SETTING BLOCKS FOR PIPES

1. Precast setting blocks for pipes shall have rectangular faces, with sufficient plan area to prevent punching of the blinding concrete or Final Surface and to provide an adequate seating for the pipes. They shall be manufactured from Grade C20 concrete using the same type of cement as in the adjacent concrete bed, and be cast in an approved mould. Blocks shall not be used until they have achieved a cube strength of 13.5 N/mm^2.

(i) BS 1142: Part 3 does not give a range of insulating board thicknesses, but these are available commercially as 12 mm, 18 mm and 24 mm. For convenience, multiples of the 18 mm board have been specified.

2.52   COMPRESSIBLE FILLER AND PACKING FOR PIPELINES

1. Compressible filler for interrupting concrete protection to pipelines shall consist of bitumen impregnated insulating board to BS 1142: Part 3 or other equally compressible material. The thickness of compressible filler shall be as follows:

Nominal bore of pipe (mm)	Thickness of compressible filler (mm)
Less than 450	18
450 – 1200	36
Exceeding 1200	54

2. Compressible packing for use between pipes and precast concrete setting blocks shall consist of bitumen damp-proof sheeting complying with BS 743.

2.53   CLAY PUDDLE

1. Clay puddle shall be impervious to water and be free from sand, grit, stones and other deleterious matter.

2. The clay on being dug shall be exposed to the air for at least 24 hours and thereafter shall be worked with water into a consistency suitable for punning. A roll of clay 300 mm long and 40 mm in diameter shall support its own weight when suspended from one end.

2.54   SEWER LININGS

(i) Appendix A of each WIs lists information to be established for particular design situations.

1. Sewer linings shall comply with the relevant provisions of the appropriate Water Industry specification (WIs) as set out below:

Type	WIs No.
Glassfibre reinforced cement (GRC)	4-12-04
Precast gunite	4-12-05
Polyethylene (PE) pipes (non-pressure applications)	4-32-05
Glassfibre reinforced plastics (GRP)	4-34-02
Polyester 'Insituform'	4-34-04
Polyester resin concrete (PRC)	4-34-05

2.55   PRECAST CONCRETE MANHOLES AND SOAKAWAYS

(i) Particular requirements from the options listed in Appendix A of BS 5911: Part 200 should be described in the Contract.

1. Precast concrete manhole and soakaway units of circular cross section shall comply with the relevant provisions of BS 5911: Part 200. Units which bed onto bases shall be manufactured so that imposed vertical loads are transmitted directly via the full wall thickness of the unit. For joints between units and the underside of slabs, joint profiles shall be capable of withstanding applied loadings from such slabs and spigot-ended sections shall only be used where the soffit of the slab is recessed to receive them.

2.56   PRECAST CONCRETE COVER FRAME SEATING RINGS

1. Precast concrete cover frame seating rings shall comply with the relevant provisions of BS 5911: Part 200.

2.57   MANHOLE COVERS AND FRAMES

(i) If a particular shape of opening is required, this should be described in the Contract.

1. Manhole covers and frames shall comply with the relevant provisions of BS 497: Part 1 and have a minimum clear opening of 600 mm. Covers and frames with minimum clear openings outside the ranges in BS 497: Part 1 shall comply with the provisions of that Standard where applicable. All manhole covers shall have closed keyways.

2.58 MANHOLE STEP IRONS

(i) For all manholes except the precast concrete type, it will be necessary to describe the size and type of manhole step irons in the Contract.

1. Step irons for manholes and other chambers shall comply with the relevant provisions of BS 1247.

2.59 GULLIES AND GULLY COVER SLABS

1. Precast concrete gullies and gully cover slabs shall comply with the relevant provisions of BS 5911: Part 2.

2. Vitrified clay gullies shall comply with the relevant provisions of BS 65.

2.60 GULLY COVERS, GRATINGS AND FRAMES

(i) Some Highway Authorities demand a particular slot configuration for gully gratings, depending upon the road gradient.

1. Gully covers, gratings and frames shall comply with the relevant provisions of BS 497: Part 1.

2.61 HYDRANTS

(i) Fire hydrants should be compatible with the requirements of the local Fire Service.

(ii) The required type of hydrant, dimensions of surface box frames and covers, and size, type and material of hydrant indicator plates should be described in the Contract.

(iii) Screw-down type hydrants with loose valve plungers may not permit the passage of swabs.

1. Hydrants, surface box frames and covers shall comply with the relevant provisions of BS 750.

2. Hydrant box covers shall be provided with recesses for lifting keys.

3. Hydrant indicator plates shall comply with the relevant provisions of BS 3251.

2.62 SURFACE BOXES AND GUARDS

(i) Particular requirements from the options listed in Appendix A of BS 5834: Part 1 should be described in the Contract, as should those from Appendix B of Parts 2 and 3.

1. Small and large surface boxes shall comply with the relevant provisions of BS 5834: Parts 2 and 3 respectively.

2. Guards and foundation units for underground stopvalves shall comply with the relevant provisions of BS 5834: Part 1.

2.63 PRECAST CONCRETE SEGMENTS FOR TUNNELS AND SHAFTS

(i) The required type of cement should be described in the Contract.

(ii) Sub-clause 7 expressly provides for the Contractor to be responsible for the adequacy of the design of the segments, insofar as it is relevant to his operations. See Clause 8(2) of the Fifth Edition. A review of current test procedures for precast concrete tunnel linings can be found in CIRIA Technical Note 104.

1. The 28 day characteristic strength of concrete used in the manufacture of segments shall be 40 N/mm^2.

2. Concrete shall be sampled and tested for compliance with the specified characteristic strength in accordance with the provisions of Clause 15 of BS 5328. Sampling shall be at a rate of not less than one sample per 20 cubic metres of fresh concrete. All segments shall have the date of manufacture clearly marked in an appropriate position at the time of manufacture.

3. Segments shall not be removed from the moulds until the concrete cube strength has reached 10 N/mm^2 and no segments shall leave the place of manufacture or be used in the Works until 28 days after casting. Copies of test cube results shall be sent to the Engineer and segments shall not be incorporated into the Permanent Works until the Engineer is satisfied that the relevant test results confirm that the concrete complies with the specified characteristic strength.

4. Segments shall be cast with such accuracy and uniformity of dimensions that all similar segments shall be interchangeable, not only within individual rings, but with corresponding segments of other rings. All surfaces of the segments shall be free from cracking, honeycombing, or other blemishes.

5. Segments shall be manufactured to the following tolerances:

Nominal dimension	Permissible deviation (mm)
Circumferential length	±1.5
Radius of curvature	±3
Thickness	±3 (on back face only)
Width	±1.5

6. Segments shall be subjected to test for water absorption in accordance with the provisions of Clause 20.2 of BS 5911: Part 100.

7. The Contractor shall ensure that segments can withstand handling, erection, and any shield thrust stresses, without cracking, spalling or distortion.

8. The clear cover of concrete over any steel reinforcement shall be not less than 12 mm and spacers shall be of rustproof material.

9. All segment joint faces shall have a caulking rebate, which shall be of minimum size 20 mm deep by 3 mm wide for bolted segments and 10 mm deep by 3 mm wide for smooth-bore segments.

10. Where grouting is described in the Contract, all segments shall have at least one grout hole of 50 mm diameter.

11. Tapered segments for curves shall comply with the general requirements of this Clause, each segment having the radius and the location of the segment within the ring, clearly marked. Segments shall be symmetrically tapered.

2.64 BITUMINOUS JOINTING STRIP
1. Jointing strip for precast concrete tunnel and shaft segments shall be bitumen-based, 3 mm minimum thickness and be suitable for the size and type of segments with which it is to be used. Where bolt holes are required, they shall accurately match, in size and position, the corresponding holes in the segments.

2.65 PACKINGS FOR TUNNELS
1. Packing pieces for joint gaps in bolted tunnel segments shall be band-sawn, knot-free softwood, preserved in accordance with Clause 2.84.

2.66 GRUMMETS
1. Grummets shall be of gel-impregnated hemp or plastic and have a thickness before compression of not less than 10 mm. Grummets shall be a tight fit on, and shall have an external diameter at least 25 mm greater than, the bolts on to which they are fitted.

2.67 LEAD
1. The chemical composition of all lead to be used for jointing or caulking shall comply with the provisions of BS 1178.

2. Lead wool shall be extruded to produce strands of triangular cross section.

2.68 STRUCTURAL STEEL
1. Structural steel sections shall comply with the relevant provisions of the appropriate British Standard, as set out below:

Type	BS
Structural steel sections	4: Part 1
Cold rolled steel sections	2994
Weldable structural steels	4360
Hot-rolled structural steel sections	4848: Parts 2 and 4
Steel tubes for general purposes	6323: Parts 2 – 7

34

(i) The required grade of steel should be described in the Contract.

ii) The requirement for piles to be coated should be deleted if no part is to be exposed on completion of the Works.

2.69   STEEL SHEET PILES

1. Steel from which steel sheet piles are rolled shall comply with the relevant provisions of BS 4360.

2. Maximum rolling margins shall be 4% above and 2.5% below the calculated masses and 75 mm over and 50 mm under the required lengths.

3. Before being driven, permanent steel sheet piles shall be wire-brushed to remove loose rust and dirt and be coated with black tar-based paint complying with BS 1070, Type B, except that piles in contact with water to be used for potable supply shall be coated with black bitumen solution to BS 3416 and 6949.

2.70   WROUGHT ALUMINIUM AND ALUMINIUM ALLOY

1. Wrought aluminium and aluminium alloys shall comply with the relevant provisions of the appropriate British Standard, as set out below:

Type	BS
Sections for structural purposes	1161
Plate, sheet and strip	1470
Drawn tube	1471
Bars, extruded round tubes and sections	1474
Ingots and castings	1490

2.71   ELECTRODES, FILLER RODS AND WIRES FOR WELDING

1. Electrodes, filler rods and wires for welding shall be compatible with the grade of steel to be welded.

2. Electrodes for the manual metal-arc welding of carbon and carbon manganese steel and stainless steel shall comply with the relevant provisions of BS 639 and BS 2926 respectively.

3. Electrode wires and fluxes for the submerged arc welding of carbon steel and medium tensile steel shall comply with the relevant provisions of BS 4165.

(i) BS 3019: Part 2 does not apply to the welding of stainless steel tubes or to sections greater than 6 mm thick.

4. Filler rods and wires for the gas-shielded arc welding of ferritic steel, austenitic stainless steel and aluminium and aluminium alloy shall comply with the relevant provisions of BS 2901: Parts 1, 2 and 4 respectively.

5. Manual welding of stainless steel shall be by the inert-gas tungsten-arc process.

2.72   NUTS, SCREWS, WASHERS AND BOLTS

(i) Any protective coatings required should be described in the Contract.

1. Mild and high strength nuts, screws, washers and bolts shall comply with the relevant provisions of the appropriate British Standard, as set out below:

Type	BS
Black hexagon bolts, screws and nuts	4190
Metal washers for general purposes	4320
High strength friction grip bolts, nuts and washers	4395; Parts 1 – 3
Black cup and countersunk head bolts and screws with nuts	4933

2. Bolting for pipes and fittings shall comply with the relevant provisions of BS 4504: Part 1, except that spheriodal graphite iron bolts for use with ductile iron pipes and fittings shall be manufactured from metal complying with the provisions of BS 2789 for Grade 500/7.

3. Bolt lengths shall be sufficient to ensure that nuts are full-threaded when tightened in their final position.

4. Stainless steel nuts, screws, washers and bolts shall be manufactured from Grade 316S31 steel complying with BS 970: Part 1 or BS 1449: Part 2.

5. Where bolting is incompatible with the material being fixed, suitable isolating washers and sleeves shall be used.

2.73 SAFETY CHAINS

1. Mild steel safety chain shall be 8 mm nominal size Grade M(4) non-calibrated chain, Type 1, complying with BS 4942: Part 2. After manufacture, mild steel safety chains shall be hot dip galvanised in accordance with BS 729.

2. Stainless steel safety chain shall be manufactured from Grade 316S31 steel complying with BS 970: Part 1. Chain links shall be welded and have an internal length not exceeding 45 mm and an internal width of between 12 mm and 18 mm. The fins caused by welding shall be removed and the weld shall be smoothly finished all round. When tested in accordance with Clause 7.3 of BS 4942: Part 2, each chain shall withstand a breaking force of 30 kN and a proof force of 15 kN.

2.74 HANDRAILS AND BALUSTERS

(i) The loading requirement of Building – use Category 6 is consistent with Table 4 of BS 6399: Part 1 for industrial balustrades. The barrier height is 1100 mm.

(ii) Where stainless steel tubes are to be bent to very small radii, it may be necessary to describe their condition as GKM(S) instead of KM.

(iii) BS 6180 also deals with permanent protective barriers designed to resist vehicular impacts.

1. Handrails and balusters shall be manufactured from material complying with the relevant provisions of the appropriate British Standard, as set out below. Protective barriers shall comply with the provisions of BS 6180 for Building – use Category 6.

Material	Handrails				Balusters			
	Solid		Tubular		Solid		Tubular	
	BS	Grade	BS	Grade	BS	Grade	BS	Grade
Mild steel	4360	43A	1387	–	4360	43A	1387	–
	–	–	or 6323 Pt 2	HFW2	–	–	or 6323 Pt 2	HFW2
Stainless steel	970 Pt1	316S31	6323 Pt8	LW17KM	970 Pt1	316S31	6323 Pt8	LW17KM
Aluminium	1474	6082	1474	6082	1490	LM6	1474	6082
	–	–	or 1471	6082	–	–	or 1471	6082

2. After manufacture, mild steel and aluminium handrails and balusters, shall be hot dip galvanised or anodised, as appropriate, in accordance with BS 729 or BS 1615, Grade AA25.

2.75 LADDERS

1. Low carbon steel ladders for vertical fixing shall comply with the relevant provision of BS 4211, Class A.

2. After fabrication, low carbon steel ladders shall be hot dip galvanised in accordance with BS 729.

3. Stainless steel ladders for vertical fixing shall be fabricated from Grade 316S31 steel complying with BS 970: Part 1 or BS 1449: Part 2 and shall comply with any dimensional provisions of BS 4211, Class A.

4. Aluminium ladders for vertical fixing shall be fabricated from Grade 6082 aluminium complying with BS 1474 and shall comply with any relevant provisions of BS 4211, Class A.

5. After fabrication, aluminium ladders shall be anodised in accordance with BS 1615, Grade AA25.

(i) The information required by Appendix B in each Part of BS 4592 should be described in the Contract.

(ii) BS 5395 gives guidance on the design and construction of stairs, ladders and walkways.

(i) Sizes and types of fixings should be described in the Contract, together with minimum requirements for edge distances, centres of fixings and embedments.

(ii) For guidance on the selection and use of fixings in concrete and masonry, see CIRIA Guide 4.

(iii) BS 6180 gives recommendations for fixing protective barriers (see Clause 2.74).

(iv) BS 5080: Part 1 does not give recommendations on the interpretation of the results of tests for the purposes of design, selection or use of fixings. CIRIA Technical Note 75 deals with loading tests on fixings in concrete.

2.76 INDUSTRIAL FLOORING, WALKWAYS AND STAIR TREADS

1. Steel and aluminium industrial open type metal flooring, walkways and stair treads shall comply with the relevant provisions of BS 4592: Parts 1, 2 and 3.

2. After fabrication, low carbon steel flooring, walkways and stair treads shall be hot dip galvanised in accordance with BS 729.

2.77 FIXINGS FOR METALWORK

1. Mild steel bolts and nuts shall be hot dip galvanised in accordance with BS 729 and stainless steel bolts and nuts shall be manufactured from Grade 316S31 steel complying with BS 970: Part 1 or BS 1449: Part 2.

2. Stainless steel proprietary fixings shall be manufactured from Grade 316S31 steel complying with BS 970: Part 1 or BS 1449: Part 2. Mild and high tensile steel proprietary fixings shall be protected in accordance with the relevant provisions of the appropriate British Standard, as set out below:

| | Type of fixing | | |
| | Cast-in, having no machined thread | Cast-in/expanding, basic major diameter of machined thread | |
Type of protection		Not exceeding 19mm	Exceeding 19mm
Hot dip galvanised	BS 729	–	–
Electroplated cadmium	BS 1706, Cd 4	BS 3382: Pt 1	BS 1706, Cd 4
Electroplated zinc	BS 1706, Zn 10	BS 3382: Pt 2	BS 1706, Zn 10

3. Where described in the Contract, axial and shear loading tests on structural fixings in concrete or masonry shall be carried out in accordance with the provisions of BS 5080: Parts 1 and 2 respectively. The safe working load shall be as described in the Contract.

4. Where fixings are incompatible with the material being fixed, suitable isolating washers and sleeves shall be used.

2.78 FIXING ACCESSORIES FOR BUILDING PURPOSES

1. Fixings for sheet, roof and wall coverings shall comply with the relevant provisions of BS 1494: Part 1.

2.79 NAILS

1. Nails shall comply with the relevant provisions of the appropriate British Standard, as set out below:

Type	BS
Steel	1202: Part 1
Copper	1202: Part 2
Aluminium	1202: Part 3

2.80 CONNECTORS FOR TIMBER

1. Connectors for timber shall comply with the relevant provisions of BS 1579.

2.81 JOIST HANGERS

1. Joist hangers for building into masonry walls, or the inner skin of cavity walls, shall comply with BS 6178, Type (b) material.

2.82 SYNTHETIC RESIN ADHESIVES

1. Synthetic resin adhesives for plywood and wood shall be phenolic and aminoplastic and comply with the relevant provisions of BS 1203 and BS 1204 respectively.

2.83 PLYWOOD

1. Plywood for general use shall comply with the relevant provisions of BS 6566: Parts 1 – 8.

(i) The required thickness, grade and type of bonding should be described in the Contract.

2.84 TIMBER AND PRESERVATION OF TIMBER

1. All timber used in the Permanent Works shall be new. Timber for structural use shall comply with BS 4978 and be of General Structural Grade. Softwood to be used for structural purposes shall only include those General Structural Grade timbers in strength class SC3 of Table 3 of BS 5268: Part 2.

2. Preservative treatment of timber, other than timber for structural purposes, shall comply with the relevant provisions of BS 5589.

3. Preservative treatment of timber for structural purposes shall comply with the relevant provisions of BS 5268: Part 5.

(i) See Regulations 8 and 10 of the Construction (General Provisions) Regulations 1961 for provisions relating to timber for excavations, shafts, tunnels and headings.

(ii) The required strength class for BS 4978 grades of softwoods should be described in the Contract.

(iii) The desired service life category should be described in the Contract.

2.85 JOINERY TIMBER

1. Timber for joinery shall comply with the relevant provisions of BS 1186: Part 1.

2. The sizes of sawn and processed softwood and hardwoods shall comply with the relevant provisions of BS 4471 and BS 5450 respectively.

2.86 WOOD TRIM

1. Wood trim in the form of architraves, skirtings, picture rails, cover fillets, quadrant, half-round and scotia moulds shall comply with the relevant provisions of BS 584.

(i) The relevant design reference in BS 584 should be described in the Contract.

2.87 WOOD FLOORING

1. Tongued and grooved softwood board and strip floorings shall be graded and sized in accordance with the relevant provisions of BS 1297.

2. Wood chipboard for flooring shall comply with BS 5669, Type II/III.

(i) The required finished thickness of flooring should be described in the Contract.

(ii) Type II chipboard is suitable where improved moisture resistance is not required.

2.88 DOORS, FRAMES AND LININGS

1. Dimensions and tolerances for wood doorsets, door leaves and frames shall be in accordance with the relevant provisions of BS 4787: Part 1. Doors, wood door frames and linings shall otherwise comply with the relevant provisions of the appropriate British Standard, as set out below:

Component	BS
Matchboarded doors	459
Wood door frames	1567
Wood door linings	1567

(i) Detailed requirements for doors should be described in the Contract.

(ii) Particular requirements for wood door frames and linings (except those for fire-check flush doors) should be described in the Contract in accordance with Appendix A of BS 1567.

2.89 LINTELS

1. Concrete, steel or timber prefabricated lintels shall comply with the relevant provisions of BS 5977: Part 2.

(i) The required type and size of lintel should be described in the Contract.

(ii) BS 5977: Part 1 gives a method for assessment of the load carried by lintels in masonry.

(i) The former British Standard for wood casement windows, BS 644: Part 1, was over twenty years old and few manufacturers produced windows to its design requirements. It was withdrawn in April 1984 and a new Standard is being drafted.

2.90 WINDOWS

1. Wood windows shall comply with the relevant provisions of British Woodworking Federation Publication 978 – 'Technical Criteria for Wood Windows'. Other windows, window surrounds and fixings shall comply with the relevant provisions of the appropriate British Standard, as set out below:

Material/Type	BS
Steel	6510
Wood surrounds for steel windows	1285
Steel window boards	6510
Aluminium alloy	4873

2.91 WINDOW SILLS

1. Precast concrete, cast stone, clayware, slate and natural stone window sills shall comply with the relevant provisions of BS 5642: Part 1.

2. Steel window sills shall comply with the relevant provisions of BS 6510.

(i) BS 952: Part 2 deals with terminology for work on glass.

(ii) described requirements for glass should be described in the Contract.

2.92 GLASS FOR GLAZING

1. Glass for glazing shall comply with the relevant provisions of BS 952: Part 1.

(i) The requirements for glazing metal frames are consistent with recommendations for non-setting glazing compounds in Clause 5.3.2.2.1 of BS 6262.

(ii) Special requirements may be necessary for putty for use with double glazing.

2.93 GLAZING MATERIALS

1. Linseed oil putty for use in glazing wooden frames shall comply with BS 544.

2. Material for use in glazing metal frames shall be a non-setting synthetic compound of oils, plasticizers and polymers, for gun, knife or strip application and shall contain an agent to produce a surface skin to minimise dirt retention.

(i) This Clause has been drafted for use in relation to painter work to BS 6150 – see Clause 6.26.

(ii) There is no current British Standard for ready mixed oil gloss paints.

(iii) The required type of priming paint should be described in the Contract.

2.94 PAINTS AND PAINTING MATERIALS FOR BUILDINGS

1. Ready mixed paints for buildings shall be external quality. Paint colours for building purposes shall comply with the relevant provisions of BS 4800.

2. Raw, refined and boiled linseed oils for paints and varnishes shall comply with the relevant provisions of BS 6900.

3. Knotting for use as an impervious covering for knots and other resinous areas shall comply with BS 1336.

4. Stopping shall comprise a mixture of one third white lead to two thirds ordinary whiting and linseed oil putty, with a small quantity of gold size added.

5. Priming paint for wood shall comply with the relevant provisions of the appropriate British Standard, as set out below:

Type	BS
Ready mixed aluminium	4756, Type II
Water-borne	5082, Type B
Solvent-borne	5358, Type B

6. Priming paint for metal shall comply with the relevant provisions of the appropriate British Standard, as set out below:

Type	BS
Lead-based	2523, Type B or C
Calcium plumbate	3698, Type A
Metallic zinc-rich (organic media)	4652

7. Paint remover shall be non-flammable, solvent-based and comply with BS 3761.

2.95 PLASTER

1. Premixed lightweight plaster shall comply with the relevant provisions of BS 1191: Part 2. Final coats shall be Type b.1 and undercoats as set out below:

Application	Type
Brickwork and blockwork	a.1 or a.3
Concrete	a.3
Metal lathing	a.2

2. Polyvinyl acetate emulsion bonding agents for internal use with BS 1191: Part 2, Type a.3 plaster shall comply with BS 5270.

2.96 METAL LATHING

1. Expanded metal and ribbed lathing for internal plastering and external rendering respectively shall comply with the relevant provisions of BS 1369: Part 1.

2.97 EXPANDED METAL ANGLE BEADS

1. Expanded metal angle beads shall comply with the relevant provisions of BS 6452: Part 1.

2.98 BOARDS FOR PANELLING

(i) The required type, grade and thickness of board should be described in the Contract.

1. Boards for panelling shall comply with the relevant provisions of the appropriate British Standard, as set out below:

Type	BS
Fibre building board – Medium board and hardboard	1142: Part 2
Fibre building board – Insulation board (softboard)	1142: Part 3
Gypsum plasterboard	1230: Part 1
Expanded polystyrene boards	3837: Part 1
Gypsum wallboard panels	4022
Rigid urethane foam – laminated board for building purposes	4841: Part 1
Rigid urethane foam – laminated board for use as a wall and ceiling insulation	4841: Part 2
Decorated laminated plastics sheet veneered boards and panels	4965
Wood chipboard	5669

2.99 WALL TILES

(i) In addition to the relevant Part of BS 6431 the type, size, thickness and colour of tiles should be described in the Contract.

1. Ceramic tiles for internal walls shall comply with the relevant provisions of BS 6431: Parts 1 – 9.

(i) Facial sizes, thickness, colour and, in the cases of floor quarries, category, should be described in the Contract.

2.100 FLOOR TILES

1. Floor tiles shall comply with the relevant provisions of the appropriate British Standard, as set out below:

Type	BS
Ceramic	6431: Parts 1 – 9
Concrete	1197: Part 2
Clay	6431
Thermoplastic	2592
PVC (vinyl) asbestos	3260
Unbacked flexible PVC	3261: Part 1
Terrazzo	4131

(i) Grade IV mastic asphalt flooring is suitable for loading sheds and heavy duty factory floors. Lower grades may be appropriate in other circumstances.

(ii) Mastic asphalts with natural rock asphalt aggregates will not normally be necessary.

(iii) Where an acidic environment is expected the Mastic Asphalt Council should be consulted for advice on suitability of limestone aggregates.

2.101 MASTIC ASPHALT

1. Mastic asphalt for building and civil engineering shall comply with the relevant provisions of BS 6925, T25, as set out below:

Application	Type
Roofing	R988
Flooring	F1076, Grade IV
Tanking	T1097
Coloured flooring	F1451, Grade IV

(i) The required type, grade, category, classification, size, group or colour of roof covering material should be described in the Contract.

2.102 ROOF COVERINGS

1. Roof coverings shall comply with the relevant provisions of the appropriate British Standard, as set out below:

Material/Type	BS
Clay tiles and fittings	402
Concrete tiles and fittings	473 & 550
Slates	680: Part 2
Asbestos-cement and cellulose – asbestos-cement flat sheets	690: Part 2
Asbestos-cement slates	690: Part 4
Asbestos-cement lining sheets and panels	690: Part 5
Felt	747

(i) This Clause is an amalgam of the recommendations of Clauses 3.14.1(4) and (5), and 2.9(1) of CP 144: Parts 3 and 4 respectively.

(ii) Where an acidic environment is expected the Mastic Asphalt Council should be consulted for advice on suitability of limestone aggregates.

2.103 MINERAL AGGREGATES FOR FLAT ROOFS

1. Mineral aggregates for the reflection of solar heat on flat built-up bitumen or mastic asphalt roofs shall be light coloured and consist of a hard limestone having a low moisture absorption characteristic, granite, gravel, calcined flint, calcite or felspar, of 10 mm nominal size.

(i) Any requirement for a different material, or thickness of sheet, should be described in the Contract.

2.104 FLASHINGS

1. Flashings shall comprise milled lead strip complying with BS 1178, Code No. 5.

(i) The type, class and grade of bricks and blocks should be described in the Contract.

2.105 BRICKS AND BLOCKS

1. Clay bricks, precast concrete masonry units and calcium silicate bricks shall comply with the relevant provisions of BS 3921, BS 6073: Parts 1 and 2 and BS 187 respectively.

(ii) IGN No. 4-10-01 deals with bricks.

2. Bricks to be used for manholes and chambers shall be solid type.

3. The shapes and dimensions of special bricks shall comply with the relevant provisions of BS 4729.

(iii) Particular requirements for airbricks and gratings from the options listed in Appendix A of BS 493 should be described in the Contract.

4. Air bricks and gratings for wall ventilation shall comply with the relevant provisions of BS 493 and shall match any surrounding bricks.

(i) DD140: Part 2 gives recommendations for the design of wall ties.

2.106   METAL TIES
1. Metal ties for cavity wall construction shall comply with the relevant provisions of BS 1243.

2.107   PERMANENT FENCING
1. Permanent fencing shall comply with the relevant provisions of the appropriate Part of BS 1722, as set out below:

(i) Where appropriate, the various Parts of BS 1722 provide for concrete for surrounding the bases of posts.

Part of BS 1722	Type of fencing
1	Chain link fences
2	Woven wire fences
3	Strained wire fences
4	Cleft chestnut pale fences
5	Close boarded fences
6	Wooden palisade fences
7	Wooden post and rail fences
8	Mild steel (low carbon steel) continuous bar fences
9	Mild steel (low carbon steel) fences with round or square verticals and flat posts and horizontals
10	Anti-intruder chain link fences
11	Woven wood and lap boarded panel fences
12	Steel palisade fences
13	Chain link fences for tennis court surrounds

2. All timber for permanent fencing shall be given preservative treatment in accordance with the provisions of the relevant Part of BS 1722.

2.108   FIELD GATES
(i) Fittings and dimensions for gates should be described in the Contract.

1. Field gates, posts and fittings shall comply with the relevant provisions of BS 3470.

2. All timber for field gates and posts shall be given preservative treatment in accordance with the provisions of BS 3470.

3. All fittings and steel field gates and posts shall be hot dip galvanised in accordance with BS 729.

2.109   STILES, BRIDLE GATES AND KISSING GATES
1. Stiles, bridle gates and kissing gates shall comply with the relevant provisions of BS 5709.

2. All timber for stiles, bridle gates, kissing gates and posts shall be given preservative treatment in accordance with the provisions of BS 5709.

3. All fittings and steel stiles, bridle gates, kissing gates and posts shall be hot dip galvanised in accordance with BS 729.

4. Concrete for surrounding the bases of posts shall be Grade C20.

(i) BS 5390 gives guidance on the choice of stone.

2.110 NATURAL STONE
1. Natural stone shall be of durable quality, uniform in texture, and free from iron bands, spots, sandholes, flaws, shakes and other imperfections which would adversely affect its strength or appearance. The dimensions of stones shall be adequate for proper coursing and bonding.

2.111 DRESSED NATURAL STONE KERBS, CHANNELS, QUADRANTS AND SETTS

(i) The required size and type of setts should be described in the Contract.

1. New dressed granite and whinstone kerbs, channels, quadrants and setts shall comply with the relevant provisions of BS 435.

2. Second-hand stone kerbs, channels, quadrants and setts shall not be excessively weathered, worn or chipped, and shall be free from all bedding and jointing materials. Faces which are to remain exposed on completion of the Works shall be free from stains.

2.112 CAST STONE

(i) The type, constituent material and colour of cast stone should be described in the Contract.

1. Cast stone shall comply with the relevant provisions of BS 1217.

2. Reconstructed stone masonry units shall comply with the relevant provisions of BS 6457.

2.113 COPING UNITS

(i) The required type of cement for cast coping units should be described in the Contract.

(ii) In areas of high air pollution, Type A slate coping units will be required.

1. Precast concrete, cast stone, clayware, natural stone and slate coping units shall comply with the relevant provisions of BS 5642: Part 2. Slate coping units shall be Type B unless otherwise described in the Contract.

2.114 PRECAST CONCRETE KERBS, CHANNELS, EDGINGS AND QUADRANTS
1. Precast concrete kerbs, channels and edgings shall be hydraulically pressed and they, and precast concrete quadrants, shall comply with BS 340. Where kerbs or channels are required to be laid to a radius of 12 m or less, components of the appropriate radius shall be used.

2.115 PRECAST CONCRETE FLAGS AND PAVING BLOCKS
1. Precast concrete flags shall be hydraulically pressed and shall comply with the relevant provisions of BS 368. Unless otherwise described in the Contract, flags shall be 50 mm thick.

2. Precast concrete paving blocks shall comply with the relevant provisions of BS 6717: Part 1.

2.116 HARDCORE

(i) Building Research Establishment Digest 276 deals with hardcore.

1. Hardcore shall consist of clean, hard, durable material, either broken stone, bricks or concrete, graded from 200 mm to 50 mm, and be free from extraneous matter.

QUALITY ASSURED PRODUCTS PREFERRED — SEE CLAUSE 2.1

2.117 GRANULAR SUB-BASE MATERIAL

1. Granular sub-base material shall be natural sands, gravels, crushed rock, crushed slag, crushed concrete or well burnt non-plastic shale. The material shall be well graded and lie within the following grading limits:

BS 410 Test sieve	Percentage by mass passing	
	Type 1	Type 2
75 mm	100	100
37.5 mm	85 – 100	85 – 100
10 mm	40 – 70	45 – 100
5 mm	25 – 45	25 – 85
600 μm	8 – 22	8 – 45
75 μm	0 – 10	0 – 10

2. Where granular sub-base material is to be used within 450 mm of the surface of any road, the Contractor shall supply to the Engineer a certificate confirming that the material has a heave not greater than 13 mm when subjected to the frost test described in the Transport and Road Research Laboratory Report LR 90.

3. Natural sands and gravels shall only be permitted in Type 2 material.

4. The particle size shall be determined by the washing and sieving method of BS 812: Part 103. The material passing a 425 μm BS sieve, when tested in accordance with BS 1377, shall be non-plastic for Type 1 and have a Plasticity Index of less than 6 for Type 2.

5. With the exception of well burnt non-plastic shale, the material shall have a 'ten per cent fines' value of 50 kN or more when tested in accordance with BS 812: Part 3.

2.118 WET-MIX MACADAM

1. Wet-mix macadam shall consist of crushed rock or crushed slag, graded in accordance with the following table:

BS 410 test sieve	Percentage by mass passing
50 mm	100
37.5 mm	95 – 100
20 mm	60 – 80
10 mm	40 – 60
5 mm	25 – 40
2.36 mm	15 – 30
600 μm	8 – 22
75 μm	0 – 8

2. The particle size shall be determined by the washing and sieving method of BS 812: Part 103.

3. Aggregate quality and cleanliness shall comply with the relevant requirements of Clause 2.10. The flakiness index shall be less than 35 when determined in accordance with BS 812: Part 105, Section 105.1.

4. The moisture content of the wet-mix macadam shall be the optimum $\pm0.5\%$ as determined in accordance with BS 5835: Part 1.

2.119 COATED MACADAM

1. Coated macadam for roads and other paved surfaces shall comply with the relevant provisions of BS 4987.

2.120 ROLLED ASPHALT

1. Hot rolled asphalt shall comply with the relevant provisions of BS 594: Part 1.

44

2.121 BITUMEN ROAD EMULSIONS

1. Bitumen road emulsions shall comply with the relevant provisions of BS 434: Part 1.

2.122 DOWEL BARS

1. Dowel bars for expansion joints in concrete shall consist of mild steel complying with the provisions of BS 4449, Grade 250.

2. Dowel bars shall be straight, free from burrs or other irregularities and shall have their sliding ends sawn. The sliding half of each dowel bar shall be painted with a thin coat of bond breaking compound, and the end of this half shall be provided with a close fitting plastic or waterproof cardboard cap at least 100 mm long, the end 20 mm of which shall be fitted with a disc of joint filler or a pad of cotton waste.

2.123 BOND BREAKING COMPOUND FOR DOWEL BARS

1. Bond breaking compound for dowel bars shall consist of a bitumen paint containing 66% of 200 pen bitumen, blended hot with 14% light creosote oil with the addition, when cold, of 20% solvent naptha. It shall in no way retard or otherwise affect the setting of concrete.

2.124 JOINT FILLER BOARD

1. Filler board for joints in concrete (other than softwood) shall comply with the tests in Clause 1015.1 of the Department of Transport's 'Specification for Highway Works' – Part 3 August 1986 (revised March 1988). Knot-free softwood, preserved in accordance with Clause 2.84 may be used for joints in concrete carriageways.

2. Holes in preformed joint filler to accommodate dowel bars shall be accurately bored or punched out to produce a sliding fit on the dowel bars.

3. The material comprising the joint filler shall be of such quality that it can be satisfactorily installed in position at the joint.

4. Adhesives used to retain preformed joint fillers in place during construction shall have no harmful effects on concrete and, except for those used in connection with softwood fillers, shall be obtained from the same manufacturer as the joint filler.

5. Preformed filler for joints in structures to retain aqueous liquids shall consist of cork granules, bound together with bitumen or synthetic resin.

2.125 JOINT SEALING COMPOUNDS AND SEALANTS

1. Joint sealing compounds shall be impermeable ductile materials of a type suitable for the conditions of exposure in which they are to be placed, and capable of providing a durable, flexible and watertight seal by adhesion to the concrete throughout the range of joint movement.

2. Hot poured joint sealants shall comply with BS 2499, Ordinary Type A1 sealant.

3. Cold poured polymer-based joint sealants shall comply with BS 5212, Normal Type N sealant.

4. Two-part polysulphide-based sealants shall comply with the relevant provisions of BS 4254. Pouring Grade shall be applied to horizontal upward-facing joints and Gun Grade to joints of any other aspect or inclination. Other two-part polymer-based sealants of Gun or Trowel Grade shall comply with the physical and test requirements of BS 4254.

5. Silicone based building sealants shall comply with the relevant provisions of BS 5889.

(i) Fuel-resistant types of sealants to BS 2499 or BS 5212 may be required where concrete surfaces are subject to regular fuel spillage.

(ii) There are no current British Standards for the cold-applied non-curing and heat-softened hand-applied types of sealant, though various such materials are available in proprietary form.

(iii) DD 69 gives a method for classifying the movement capability of joint sealants, other than those to BS 4254 and BS 5215.

(iv) BS 6213 gives guidance on the selection of constructional sealants and DD 121 on classification.

(v) In certain circumstances polyurethane-based sealants (for which there are no current British Standards) may be more resistant to biodegradation than polysulphide-based ones.

(vi) CIRIA Technical Note 128 deals with civil engineering sealants in wet conditions.

6. Primers for use with joint sealants shall be compatible with, and obtained from the same manufacturers as, the adjacent sealant. Primers shall have no harmful effects on concrete.

7. Sealants and primers which will be in contact with water to be used for potable supply shall not impart to water taste, colour, or any effect known to be harmful to health, and shall be resistant to bacterial growth.

8. Sealants and primers which will be in contact with sewage or sewage sludge shall be resistant to biodegradation.

2.126 WATERSTOPS

1. Plasticized PVC waterstops shall comply with the relevant provisions of WIs No. 4-31-02.

(i) The properties of PVC waterstops are temperature and formulation dependent. Manufacturers' recommendations for storage, handling, installation and use, particularly at temperatures below 0°C, should be obtained.

(ii) IGN No. 4-31-03 gives guidance on joint design and installation of PVC waterstops in water retaining structures.

2. Rubber waterstops shall have the following properties when tested in accordance with the relevant Part of BS 903:

Property	Requirement
Density	1100 kg/m^3 ($\pm$5%)
Hardness	60 – 70 IRHD
Tensile strength	not less than 20 N/mm^2
Elongation at break point	not less than 450%
Water absorption (48 hours immersion)	not exceeding 5%

3. Rubber waterstops shall be suitable for storage, handling, installation and service within a temperature range of 0°C to +40°C.

2.127 DAMP PROOF COURSE

(i) BS 743 provides for damp proof courses of materials other than bitumen, except for polythene, which is covered by BS 6515.

1. Damp proof course shall be bitumen with hessian base complying with BS 6398, Class A.

3. Unless otherwise described in the Contract, the cementitious content of concrete shall not exceed 400 kg/m³ or 450 kg/m³ where pfa forms a cementitious component and the structure is designed to retain an aqueous liquid. In any structural member, the maximum water/cementitious ratio and the minimum cementitious content of the concrete mix shall be in accordance with the following table, for the relevant exposure condition and nominal cover. Concrete in members of structures that are to retain an aqueous liquid shall have a maximum free water/cementitous ratio of 0.55.

Exposure condition	Nominal cover (mm)			
Mild	20	20	20	20
Moderate	35	30	25	20
Severe	–	40	30	25
Very severe	–	50	40	30
Max. free water/cementitious ratio	0.60	0.55	0.50	0.45
Min. cementitious content (kg/m³)	300	325	350	400

4. Where the Contract requires aggregates of nominal size other than 20 mm to be used, the minimum cementitious content in Clause 4.3.3 shall be modified as follows:

Nominal maximum aggregate size (mm)	Adjustments to mininum cementitious content in Clause 4.3.3 (kg/m³)
10	+40
14	+20
40	−30

5. The maximum size of aggregate in any structural member shall not exceed 25% of the minimum thickness of the member.

4.4 CONCRETE MIXES CONTAINING PFA

1. The free water/cementitious ratio of concrete mixes containing pfa shall be reduced in relation to the pfa content, consistent with maintenance of the required workability, and shall not exceed 0.50 for concrete designed to retain an aqueous liquid.

2. Sulphate-resisting cement shall not be used in concrete mixes containing pfa.

4.5 CONCRETE MIXES CONTAINING GGBS

1. Sulphate-resisting cement shall not be used in concrete mixes containing ggbs.

4.6 POROUS NO-FINES CONCRETE

1. Porous no-fines concrete shall contain ordinary Portland cement and 20 mm single sized aggregate complying with BS 882, in a proportion of 1:10 by mass.

2. The concrete shall be mixed to a uniform colour and consistency with the addition of water sufficient only to coat all of the aggregate without forming excess grout.

3. The concrete shall not be mechanically vibrated or excessively worked when placed.

4.7 AIR-ENTRAINED CONCRETE

(i) Air entraining admixtures used in conjunction with pfa can give rise to very variable air content.

(ii) The percentages in Clause 4.7.1 are consistent with the recommendations of Clause 6.2.3.2 of BS 8110.

(iii) Compliance criteria for the air content of concrete are set out in Clause 16.7 of BS 5328.

1. Where air-entrained concrete is required, it shall have an average air content by volume of the fresh concrete at the time of placing in accordance with the following table:

Nominal maximum aggregate size (mm)	Average air content of concrete (%)
10	7
14	6
20	5
40	4

4.8 CHLORIDE CONTENT

(i) The limits for chloride ion content are consistent with Clause 6.2.5.2 of BS 8110: Part 1.

1. Calcium chloride or admixtures containing calcium chloride shall not be used in the production of reinforced concrete or concrete which is to contain embedded metal.

2. Steam-cured concrete shall not contain chloride ions, derived from all its constituents, in excess of 0.1% by mass of its cementitious content. The percentage for all other concrete containing embedded metal in the final work shall not exceed the following:

Portland cement concrete, rapid hardening Portland cement concrete, or combinations with ggbs or pfa — 0.4, save that the proportion may be up to 0.5 in not more than 5% of the test results.

Concrete made with sulphate-resisting or supersulphated cement — 0.2

4.9 ADJUSTMENTS TO DESIGNED MIX PROPORTIONS

1. During production of designed mix concrete, the Contractor shall adjust mix proportions within the limits prescribed in BS 5328 to achieve the required strength and workability.

4.10 TRIAL MIXES

(i) Where it is not practicable to carry out full scale trials, special reference should be made in the Contract to laboratory scale mixes.

(ii) Sufficient information should be derived from the trial mixes to ensure that the concrete will meet the specified requirements, including optional items under Clause 12.3 of BS 5328. It may also be necessary to specify water absorption tests for structures designed to retain an aqueous liquid.

(iii) The criteria in Clause 4.10.3 apply to trial mixes only. For assessment of samples taken during construction see Clause 16.2.1 of BS 5328.

1. Where trial mixes are required, three separate batches of concrete shall be made using materials typical of the proposed source of supply and, where practicable, under fullscale production conditions.

2. The workability of each of the trial batches shall be determined and three cubes made from each batch for test at 28 days.

3. The trial mix proportions for structural concrete shall be approved if the average compressive strength of the nine cubes tested at 28 days exceeds the required characteristic strength by not less than 10 N/mm^2 for Grade C20 concrete or higher, or 5 N/mm^2 for Grade C15 concrete or lower, provided that the strength determined from any one cube does not fall below the required characteristic strength by more than 1 N/mm^2 or 10% (whichever is the greater).

4. Additional sets of cubes from each batch may be required for tests at an earlier age.

5. Where required, two further trial mix batches shall be made with cementitious material and typical surface-dry aggregates to show that any stated maximum free water/cementitious ratio is not exceeded. The proposed mix proportions shall not be accepted unless both batches have the correct cementitious content and a free water/cementitious ratio below the maximum specified value for the intended degree of workability. For this purpose, existing test reports may be used instead of trial mixes, if the Engineer is satisfied that the materials to be incorporated in the concrete are to be similar to those used in the tests.

4.11 WORKABILITY

1. Workability of fresh concrete shall be such that the concrete can be handled and placed without segregation and, after compaction, can completely fill the formwork and surround all reinforcement and ducts.

2. The quantity of water used shall not exceed that required to produce a concrete with appropriate workability to be placed and compacted in the required location.

4.12 TRANSPORTING, PLACING AND COMPACTING

(i) Any requirements for placing concrete in special sequence, e.g. by alternate bay construction, should be described in the Contract.

1. Concrete shall be transported from the mixer and placed in the Works as rapidly as practicable by methods which will prevent the segregation or loss of any of the ingredients and will maintain the required workability. It shall be deposited as nearly as practicable in its final position and all equipment for transporting concrete shall be kept clean.

2. The Contractor shall give adequate notice to the Engineer of his intention to commence concreting.

3. Concrete shall be thoroughly compacted in its final position within 30 minutes of discharge from the mixer, unless carried in purpose-made agitators operating continuously, when the time shall be within 2 hours of the introduction of the cement to the mix and within 30 minutes of the discharge from the agitator.

4. The plant used for compaction shall be operated continuously during the placing of each batch of concrete until the expulsion of air has virtually ceased, and in a manner which does not promote segregation of the ingredients.

5. Whenever vibration has to be applied externally, the design of formwork and disposition of vibrators shall be such as to ensure efficient compaction and to avoid surface blemishes.

4.13 CONCRETING IN COLD WEATHER

1. Concreting at ambient temperatures below 2°C may be carried out only if the following conditions are met:

(a) the aggregates and water used in the mix shall be free from snow, ice and frost.

(b) before placing concrete, the formwork, reinforcement and any surface with which the fresh concrete will be in contact shall be free from snow, ice and frost and shall be at a temperature above 0°C.

(c) the initial temperature of the concrete at the time of placing shall be at least 5°C, and

(d) the temperature at the surface of the concrete shall be maintained at not less than 5°C at any point until the concrete reaches a strength of 5 N/mm^2, as confirmed by tests on cubes matured under similar conditions.

2. The Contractor shall take precautions to prevent the temperature of any concrete falling to 0°C during the first five days after placing.

4.14 CONCRETE TEMPERATURE

1. The resultant temperature of the combined materials in any batch of concrete at the point and time of delivery to the Works shall not exceed 6°C above the prevailing shade temperature, when the latter is over 21°C.

2. The Contractor shall not permit any cement to come into contact with water at a temperature greater than 60°C.

3. Where the temperature of the fresh concrete is likely to exceed 32°C, concreting shall not be permitted unless measures are taken to keep the temperature below that level.

4.15 CURING

(i) Consideration may have to be given to measures to prevent thermal cracking where a temperature differential in excess of 20°C is likely to occur, for example by extending striking times for the formwork.

(ii) The table in Clause 4.15.1 is taken from Table 6.5 of BS 8110: Part 1 and the ambient conditions therefore have the following meanings:

  good: damp and protected (relative humidity greater than 80%; protected from sun and wind).

  average: intermediate between good and poor.

  poor: dry or unprotected (relative humidity less than 50%; not protected from sun and wind).

1. Concrete shall be cured for a period not less than that given in the following table, by methods that shall ensure that cracking, distortion and efflorescence are minimised:

Type of cement	Ambient conditions after casting	Minimum period of curing and protection	
		5°C to 10°C	Above 10°C
BS 12 and BS 4027	Average	4 days	3 days
	Poor	6 days	4 days
All except BS 12 and BS 4027 and all with pfa or ggbs	Average		
	Poor	10 days	7 days
All	Good	No special requirements	

2. In cold weather, when the temperature of freshly placed concrete may approach 0°C, water curing shall not be employed.

3. Components which are intended to have a similar exposed surface finish shall receive the same treatment.

4.16 RECORDS OF CONCRETING

1. The Contractor shall keep up to date records of the dates and times when concreting is carried out and of the weather and temperatures at those times. The records shall be available for inspection by the Engineer.

4.17 CONSTRUCTION OF FORMWORK

(i) BS 5975 gives recommendations as to standards of good practice in formwork construction.

(ii) The positioning and detailing of movement joints should be described in the Contract.

(iii) Any special conditions relating to the re-use of forms, insofar as the materials of construction and repairs between uses may affect the colour and surface finish of exposed surfaces, should be described in the Contract.

(iv) Any special requirements regarding chamfers to internal and external angles should be described in the Contract.

1. Formwork shall be sufficiently rigid and tight to prevent loss of mortar from the concrete and to maintain the correct position, shape and dimensions of the finished work. It shall be so constructed as to be removable from the cast concrete without shock or damage.

2. The forms shall be capable of producing a consistent quality of surface as described in the Contract.

3. Where holes are required in forms to accommodate projecting reinforcement, fixing devices or other built-in items, precautions shall be taken to prevent loss of mortar matrix.

4. Formwork shall give access for the preparation of joint surfaces before the concrete has hardened.

5. For the purposes of compliance with the provisions of Clause 4.19.4, the Contractor's method of constructing formwork shall allow for props to soffit forms to remain in position continuously for the period described.

4.18 CLEANING AND TREATMENT OF FORMS

1. The interiors of all forms shall be thoroughly cleaned out before any concrete is placed. The faces of the forms in contact with the concrete shall be clean and treated with a suitable release agent, where applicable.

2. Where a concrete surface is to be permanently exposed, only one release agent shall be used throughout the entire area. Release agents shall be applied evenly and contact with reinforcement and other embedded items avoided. Where the concrete surface is to receive an applied finish, care shall be taken to ensure the compatability of the release agent with the finish.

4.19 STRIKING OF FORMWORK

(i) As the removal of formwork is dependent upon the Contractor's method of working, the Engineer may wish to agree a formal procedure for determining striking times based on CIRIA Report 67 – Tables of Minimum Striking Times for Soffit and Vertical Formwork and Report 73 Formwork Striking Times – Methods of Assessment.

1. Formwork shall be removed without shock to or disturbance of the concrete.

2. Formwork to vertical surfaces or sloping formwork not supporting concrete in flexure shall not be removed until, as may be relevant, the following criteria are met:

(a) a minimum period shall have elapsed since the concrete was poured equivalent to 11 hours at 15°C for unsealed plywood forms, or 8 hours at 15°C for impermeable forms.

(ii) It should be noted that 11 hours at 15°C is equivalent to:
8 hours at 20°C
15 hours at 10°C
24 hours at 5°C

8 hours at 15°C is equivalent to
6 hours at 20°C
12 hours at 10°C
18 hours at 5°C

(b) the concrete strength shall be sufficient to meet any wind loading upon the concrete likely to arise at the time when the formwork is removed.

3. Formwork supporting concrete in flexure shall not be removed until the concrete strength (as confirmed by tests on cubes cured under representative conditions) has reached 10 N/mm^2, or twice the stress to which the concrete will then be subjected, whichever is the greater.

(iii) Any requirement for the control of thermal cracking should be described in the Contract.

4. In the absence of cube test results or any formal procedure agreed in writing with the Engineer, the periods before striking given in the following table shall be used:

Type of formwork	Ordinary Portland and sulphate resisting cement concrete		Rapid hardening Portland cement concrete	
	Mean ambient temperature		Mean ambient temperature	
	15°C	5°C	15°C	5°C
Soffit forms to slabs and beams	5 days	7 days	4 days	7 days
Props to slabs and beams	10 days	15 days	10 days	15 days
When other types of cement, combinations of cement or admixtures are used, or when the temperature varies from those above, the periods shall be adjusted in order to achieve the equivalent minimum maturity at striking.				

5. The Contractor shall give adequate notice to the Engineer of his intention to strike formwork.

4.20 SLOPING FORMWORK

(i) Any requirement for top formwork at slopes flatter than 30° to the horizontal should be described in the Contract.

1. Top formwork shall be provided to slopes 30° or more from the horizontal.

4.21 CUTTING AND BENDING OF REINFORCEMENT

1. Cutting and bending of reinforcement shall be in accordance with BS 4466 and shall be done without the application of heat and in a temperature of not less than 5°C. Bends shall have a substantially constant curvature.

2. Reinforcement shall not be straightened or rebent without the approval of the Engineer. If permission is given to bend projecting reinforcement, care shall be taken not to damage the concrete and to ensure that the radius is not less than the minimum specified in BS 4466.

4.22 FIXING OF REINFORCEMENT

1. Reinforcement shall be firmly supported in position and secured against displacement.

2. Non-structural connections for the positioning of reinforcement shall be made with tying wire or other fixing devices. Precautions shall be taken to ensure that projecting ends of ties or clips do not encroach into the concrete cover.

3. The concrete cover shall be not less than the required cover minus 5 mm and, where reinforcement is located in relation to only one face of a member, not more than the required cover plus:

5 mm for bars up to and including 12 mm size
10 mm for bars over 12 mm up to and including 25 mm size
15 mm for bars over 25 mm size.

4.23 SURFACE CONDITION OF REINFORCEMENT

(i) Any protection required for steel left projecting should be described in the Contract.

1. Concrete shall not be placed until reinforcement is free from any substance which might adversely affect the steel or concrete chemically or reduce the bond.

4.24 LAPS AND JOINTS
1. Laps and joints in reinforcement shall be made only at the positions described in the Contract or as agreed by the Engineer.

4.25 WELDING OF REINFORCEMENT
1. Reinforcement shall not be welded on Site except where described in or permitted under the Contract. All welding procedures shall be subject to the prior approval of the Engineer in writing.

4.26 BUILT-IN ITEMS
1. Where pipes, sleeves, water bars or other items are built into concrete, they shall be rigidly secured in position to prevent movement and shall be free from external coatings which might reduce the bond. The Contractor shall take precautions to prevent the formation of air pockets, voids or other defects whilst the concrete is being placed.

4.27 CONSTRUCTION JOINTS

(i) The positioning and form of construction joints in structures designed to retain an aqueous liquid should be with a view to the control of cracking. See BS 8007, Section 5.

1. Except where construction joints in concrete are described in the Contract, the Contractor shall obtain the Engineer's approval to the positions and details of such joints before any work is commenced.

2. Joint lines shall be arranged to coincide wherever possible with features of the finished work.

3. Concreting shall be carried out continuously up to construction joints.

4. Concrete shall not be allowed to taper off to a thickness of less than 50 mm. Vertical joints shall be formed against a stop board suitably notched to accommodate the reinforcement. The top surface of each lift of concrete shall be straight and level unless described otherwise in the Contract.

5. Where a kicker is used, it shall be at least 70 mm high and shall be incorporated with the previous concrete.

6. The surface of any concrete against which new concrete is to be cast shall be free from laitance and shall be roughened to the extent that the large aggregate is exposed but not disturbed. The joint surface shall be cleaned immediately before the fresh concrete is placed against it.

7. Where practicable, such preparation of joints shall be carried out when the concrete has set but not hardened.

4.28 SURFACE FINISHES PRODUCED WITHOUT FORMWORK

Screeded Finish

1. The concrete shall be levelled and screeded to produce a uniform plain or ridged surface as required. No further work shall be applied to the surface unless it is a first stage for a Wood Float or Steel Trowel Finish.

Wood Float Finish

2. The Screeded Finish shall be wood floated under light pressure to eliminate surface irregularities.

Steel Trowel Finish

3. When the moisture film has disappeared and the concrete has hardened sufficiently to prevent laitance from being worked to the surface, the surface to the Wood Float Finish shall be steel-trowelled under firm pressure to produce a dense, smooth, uniform surface free from trowel marks.

4. Where the type of finish is not given it shall be Wood Float Finish.

4.29 SURFACE FINISHES PRODUCED WITH FORMWORK

Rough Finish

1. This finish shall be obtained by the use of moulds or properly designed forms of closely-jointed sawn boards. The surface shall be free from substantial voids, honeycombing or other large blemishes.

Fair Finish

2. This finish shall be obtained from forms designed to produce a hard smooth surface with true, clean arrises. Only very minor surface blemishes shall be permitted and there shall be no staining or discolouration. Any projections shall be removed and the surface made good.

Fair Worked Finish

3. This finish shall be obtained by first producing a Fair Finish and then filling all surface blemishes with a fresh, specially prepared cement and fine aggregate paste whilst the concrete is still green where possible. After the concrete has been properly cured, the faces shall be rubbed down, if required, to produce a smooth and even surface. If the surface is to be exposed in the final work, every effort shall be made to match the colour of the concrete.

4.30 HIGH STRENGTH CONCRETE TOPPING
1. High strength concrete topping (granolithic finish) shall be provided, laid and finished in accordance with the relevant provisions of BS 8204: Part 2.

4.31 TIE BOLTS FOR FORMWORK
1. Only tie bolts which avoid embedding any metal parts permanently within 50 mm of the concrete surface shall be permitted. Voids remaining after the removal of all or part of each tie bolt shall be filled flush with the surrounding concrete using a freshly prepared cement and fine aggregate paste. In the case of structures designed to retain an aqueous liquid, the contractor shall ensure that the measures adopted shall not impair the watertightness of the structure.

4.32 MARKING OF PRECAST CONCRETE COMPONENTS
1. Where appropriate, indelible indentification and orientation marks shall be put on all precast concrete components in such a position that the marks shall not show or be exposed in the finished work.

4.33 TOLERANCES FOR CONCRETE SURFACES
1. Concrete surfaces in the final work shall not vary from those described in the Contract to an extent readily observable by eye, shall have no abrupt irregularities and, subject to retaining the required concrete cover to reinforcement, other deviations shall be no more than the following permissible amounts:

Type of Finish	Deviation from line, level, verticality, cross sectional dimension or length (mm)
Screeded or Rough	10
Any other	5

SECTION 5

CONSTRUCTION OF PIPELINES, TUNNELS AND ANCILLARY WORKS

5.1 PIPELAYING GENERALLY

1. Where socketed pipes are required to be laid on a granular or sand bed, or directly on a trench bottom, joint holes shall be formed in the bedding material or excavated Final Surface to ensure that each pipe is uniformly supported throughout the length of its barrel and to enable the joint to be made.

2. Pipes shall be laid on setting blocks only where a concrete bed or cradle is used.

3. Where pipes are required to be bedded directly on the trench bottom, the Final Surface shall be trimmed and levelled to provide even bedding of the pipeline and shall be free from all extraneous matter that may damage the pipe, pipe coating, or sleeving.

4. No protective cap, disc or other appliance on the end of a pipe or fitting shall be removed permanently until the pipe or fitting which it protects is about to be jointed. Pipes and fittings, including any lining or sheathing, shall be examined for damage and the joint surfaces and components shall be cleaned immediately before laying.

5. Suitable measures shall be taken to prevent soil or other material from entering pipes, and to anchor each pipe to prevent flotation or other movement before the Works are complete.

6. Where pipeline marker tape is specified, it shall be laid between 100 mm and 300 mm above the pipe. Where a tracer system is specified it shall be continuous and adequately secured to valves and fittings.

(i) The following publications give recommendations on standards of good practice for the installation of pipelines on land:

BS 8010
Part 1   Pipelines on land:
          General
Section 2.1 Ductile Iron
Section 2.3 Asbestos-cement
Section 2.4 Prestressed Concrete
          pressure pipelines

CP2010
Part 2   Steel Pipelines

BS 5927 Laying of Asbestos-
         Cement Pipelines

BS 5955: Part 6 Plastics Pipework
         (Gravity)

BS 8005 Sewerage: Part 1

'Principles of Laying Water Mains' and 'Principles of Laying Sewers', guides to good site practice published by the WAA Sewers and Water Mains Committee.

CP 312 Plastics pipework (thermo-plastics materials): Parts 1, 2 and 3.

(ii) For handling of pipes, see Clause 2.3.

(iii) For minimum clearances to pipes in rock trenches, see Clause 3.1.

(iv) For details of marker tapes see Clause 2.42.

(i) When puddled clay stanks are required, these should be described in the Contract.

5.2 GRANULAR BEDDING

1. Granular bedding for pipes shall be constructed by spreading and compacting granular bedding material over the full width of the pipe trench. After the pipes have been laid, additional granular material shall, if required, be placed and compacted equally on each side of the pipes and, where practicable, this shall be done in sequence with the removal of the trench supports.

5.3 CONCRETE PROTECTION TO PIPES

1. Pipes to be bedded on or cradled with concrete shall be supported on precast concrete setting blocks, the top face of each block being covered with two layers of compressible packing in accordance with Clause 2.52.

2. Concrete provided as a protection to pipes shall be Grade C20, placed to the required depth in one operation.

3. Where pipes with flexible joints are used, the concrete protection shall be interrupted over its full cross section at intervals not exceeding 8 m by a shaped compressible filler in accordance with Clause 2.52. These interruptions shall coincide with pipe joints.

4. Rapid hardening cement shall not be used in concrete for the protection of plastics pipe.

5. Plastics pipes shall be wrapped with a layer of plastic sheeting complying with Clause 2.26.1 before being surrounded by concrete.

5.4 COMPLETION OF PIPE SURROUND WITH TYPE B MATERIAL

1. After completion of the relevant operations in Clauses 5.1, 5.2 and 5.3, Type B fill material shall, where required, be placed and compacted over the full width of the trench in layers not exceeding 150 mm before compaction, to a minimum finished thickness of 300 mm above the crown of the pipes.

2. Subsequent filling shall then be carried out as specified in Clause 3.7.

5.5 PIPELAYING IN HEADINGS

(i) See also Clauses 3.1, 5.1 and 5.3.

1. Pipes to be laid in headings shall be supplied in lengths suitable for handling, jointing and packing within the working space available.

2. Headings shall be driven from shaft to shaft or in such other lengths as may be described in the Contract before any pipelaying is commenced.

3. After pipelaying, headings shall be packed solid with Grade C20 concrete so as to fill all voids. Where manual packing is employed, each pipe shall be surrounded before laying and jointing the next pipe.

4. Where grouting of headings is described in the Contract, grouting pipes shall be left in the top of the heading projecting behind each head tree and the whole grouted solid with grout Class G1. Grouting shall be carried out at the end of each shift or after three settings have been packed, whichever is the shorter interval.

5.6 THRUST BLOCKS

(i) Thrust blocks should either be described in the Contract or constructed in accordance with the Engineer's instructions on Site.

1. Except where self anchoring joints are used, thrusts from bends and branches in pressure pipelines shall be resisted by concrete thrust blocks cast in contact with undisturbed ground.

2. Any additional excavation required to accommodate thrust blocks shall be carried out after the bend or branch is in position and the thrust face shall be trimmed back to remove all loose or weathered material immediately prior to concreting.

3. Thrust blocks shall be allowed to develop adequate strength before any internal pressure is applied to the pipeline.

4. Rapid hardening cement shall not be used in concrete for thrust blocks to plastics pipe.

5. Plastics pipes shall be wrapped with a layer of plastic sheeting complying with Clause 2.26.1 before being surrounded by concrete.

5.7 PIPE JOINTING GENERALLY

(i) Proprietary joints are required to be made in accordance with the manufacturers' instructions. See Clause 2.3.

(ii) Any special requirements for filling the joint annulus should be described in the Contract.

1. Pipe jointing surfaces and components shall be kept clean and free from extraneous matter until the joints have been made or assembled. Care shall be taken to ensure that there is no ingress of grout or other extraneous material into the joint annulus after the joint has been made.

(iii) The remaining flexibility is required for any subsequent settlement or ground movement.

2. Where pipes with flexible joints are required to be laid to curves, the deflection at any joint as laid shall not exceed three quarters of the maximum deflection recommended by the manufacturer.

5.8 WELDED JOINTS IN PLASTICS PIPES

(i) Different types of PE 'soften' at different temperatures and when soft have different viscosities which may impair the jointing process.

(ii) Joints in HDPE and MDPE should be made in accordance with the manufacturers' instructions. See Clause 2.3 .

(iii) Any requirement for weld tests should be described in the Contract.

(iv) IGN No. 4-31-01 deals with uPVC pipe jointing.

1. Fusion welded joints in high density and medium density polyethylene pipes shall be made only between pipes having the same physical characteristics. Joints between pipes from different manufacturers shall only be made with the specific approval of the Engineer.

2. Site fusion jointing shall be made in accordance with WIs No. 4-32-08.

3. When solvent welded uPVC pipes are jointed outside the trench, they shall not be lowered into place until the period recommended by the manufacturer for complete setting of the joints has elapsed.

4. A pipe section containing a completed weld shall achieve the same strength characteristics as the parent pipe.

5.9 FLANGED JOINTS

(i) Where the Contractor is not required to provide nuts, bolts, washers and/or jointing gaskets, this should be described in the Contract.

(ii) Any special requirements for the type of flange gasket should be described in the Contract. See also Clause 2.48.

1. Flanges shall be properly aligned before any bolts are tightened.

2. Jointing compounds shall not be used when making flanged joints, except that, to facilitate the making of vertical joints, gaskets may be secured temporarily to one flange face by a minimum quantity of clear rubber solution. Bolt threads shall be treated with graphite paste and the nuts tightened evenly in diametrically opposite pairs.

5.10 OGEE JOINTS

(i) Any required jointing material (mastic or cement mortar) should be described in the Contract.

1. Ogee joints shall be so made that the required jointing material fills the joint cavity. Any surplus jointing material extruded inside the barrel shall be trimmed off and, where practicable, pointed on completion.

5.11 CEMENT MORTAR JOINTS

(i) This Clause is intended to refer only to pipes cut on Site.

1. In making yarn and mortar joints for pipes or fittings, the spigot shall be entered into the socket of the last pipe laid until it bears on the back face of the socket, and it shall be centred in the socket. Two turns of tarred yarn shall then be caulked into the back of the socket with a proper caulking tool and Class M1 cement mortar shall be pressed into the joint to fill the socket and shall be bevelled off at 45° from the outside edge of the socket.

5.12 RUN LEAD JOINTS

1. Run lead joints shall be made by forcing home strands of white sterilised jute piping yarn, with proper irons, to the back of the socket cavity leaving a space of 75 mm (60 mm for pipes of 300 mm nominal bore and below) measured from the socket face. The socket face shall then be encircled by a suitable clip or gasket and the joint cavity filled with molten lead poured in one running. After cooling, the lead shall be set up with proper caulking tools and neatly finished with the face of the lead 2 mm back from the socket face. In the case of pipes over 750 mm diameter, the socket and spigot shall be heated before the joint is run.

5.13 PROTECTION OF FERROUS PIPES, JOINTS AND FITTINGS

General

(i) For application of protection see Clause 2.3.2.

1. Pipes joints and fittings shall be cleaned and all loose rust removed before protection is applied.

External protection – bolted joints and fittings

2. External protection for bolted joints and fittings shall comprise:

P1   The application of approved mastic paste in sufficient quantity to cover all protruding edges, bolt heads and sharp edges of flanges, to give a smooth external profile. The joint or fitting shall be wrapped with two separate layers of approved protective tape wound spirally with a minimum half width overlap. The taping shall extend along 150 mm of the barrel of the pipe on each side of the joint or fitting.

or

P2   The application of a self-adhesive rubber-based cold-applied tape wrap combined with a thick PVC backing. Where bolt heads, flanges and other projections arise a moulding putty shall be used to give a smooth external profile. The joint or fitting shall be wrapped with two separate layers of protective tape wrap spirally applied with minimum of half width overlap. The tape shall extend along 150 mm of the barrel of the pipe on each side of joint or fitting.

or

P3   The application of heat shrink sleeves.

External protection – ductile iron pipes

3. External protection for ductile iron pipes shall comprise:

P4   The covering of the pipes with lay flat polythene sleeving securely held in place with adhesive tape at pipe joints and intermediate positions.

or

P5   The factory application of plastic sleeving. Protection of joints and repair to any damage shall be carried out on Site.

or

P6   Painting the external surface as described in the Contract.

or

(ii) For guidance on cathodic protection see CP 1021 and 'Guides to practice in corrosion control – No 9, Cathodic Protection' published by the National Corrosion Service of the National Physical Laboratory.

P7   Cathodic protection of either impressed current or sacrificial anode and shall be designed and installed in accordance with a design approved by the Engineer.

4. Protection for steel pipes shall be provided as follows:

(a)   Internal protection

Where pipes have a bituminous lining in which a gap has been left for the joint to be made, the lining shall be completed in accordance with recommendations issued by British Steel Corporation, unless otherwise described in the Contract.

(iii) The type of external protection required should be described in the Contract.

(b)   External protection

Protection shall comprise bitumen trowelled on to the external surface of the joint followed, where appropriate, by a spiral wrap of heavy duty glass fibre tape bonded with hot bituminous composition, all in accordance with recommendations issued by British Steel Corporation, unless otherwise described in the Contract.

5.14 CUTTING PIPES

1. Pipes shall be cut by a method which provides a clean square profile, without splitting or fracturing the pipe wall, and which causes minimal damage to any protective coating. Where necessary, the cut ends of pipes shall be formed to the tapers and chamfers suitable for the type of joint to be used and any protective coatings shall be made good.

2. Where ductile pipes are to be cut to form non-standard lengths, the Contractor shall comply with the manufacturer's recommendations in respect of ovality correction and tolerances to the cut spigot end.

5.15 PRECAST CONCRETE MANHOLES

1. Precast concrete chamber and shaft sections shall be constructed with step irons, ladders or slabs aligned correctly.

2. Joints shall be made so that the required jointing material fills the joint cavity. Any surplus jointing material extruded inside the chamber or shaft shall be trimmed off and joints shall be pointed on completion.

3. Where manholes are to have a concrete surround, the concrete shall be Grade C20 and the height of each concrete pour shall not exceed 2 m. Each construction joint shall break joint with that of the chamber or shaft sections by at least 150 mm.

5.16 PRECAST CONCRETE SEGMENTAL MANHOLES

1. Precast concrete segmental manholes shall be constructed in accordance with the relevant provisions of Clauses 5.25 to 5.27 and 5.29 to 5.35.

5.17 BRICK AND IN-SITU CONCRETE MANHOLES AND CHAMBERS

1. Manholes and chambers constructed in brickwork or in-situ concrete shall comply with the relevant provisions of Sections 4 and 6 respectively.

5.18 INVERTS AND BENCHING

1. Manhole inverts and benchings shall be formed of the materials described in the Contract and where there is no change of diameter, the invert shall follow the same gradient as the outgoing sewer.

2. Where inverts and benchings are to be formed of in-situ concrete or high strength concrete topping (granolithic finish), the relevant provisions of Section 4 shall apply.

3. Where a high strength concrete topping (granolithic finish) is required, the invert and benching shall be formed in Grade C20 concrete with a Screeded Finish or Rough Finish as required, and the concrete topping shall be applied as soon as practicable thereafter.

4. Where the finished surface is to be in-situ concrete, the concrete shall be Grade C20 with a Steel Trowel or Fair Worked Finish as required.

5. Where the inverts of both manhole and sewer are constructed of brickwork, there shall be no break in bond between the two.

5.19 PIPES AND JOINTS ADJACENT TO STRUCTURES

1. Except where the construction is by tunnelling, heading or pipe jacking, a flexible joint shall be provided as close as is feasible to the outside face of any structure into which the pipe is built, compatible with the satisfactory completion and subsequent movement of the joint.

2. The length of the next pipe (rocker pipe) away from the structure shall be in the range 0.5 m to 0.75 m for pipes up to 450 mm nominal bore and shall not exceed 1 m for pipes up to 750 mm nominal bore.

(i) The type of jointing material should be described in the Contract.

(i) The benching material and surface finish should be described in the Contract.

(ii) The Surface Finishes referred to are specified in Clauses 4.28 and 4.29.

(i) The requirements for rocker pipes are consistent with BS 8005: Part 1.

3. A pipeline may, where practicable, be laid through a manhole and the crown broken out to the half diameter, provided flexible joints are situated on each side, no further than 600 mm from the inner face of the manhole wall, and that adjacent pipes comply with Sub-clause 2 of this Clause.

5.20 WATERTIGHTNESS OF MANHOLES AND CHAMBERS
1. Manholes and chambers shall be substantially watertight, with no identifiable flow of water penetrating the Permanent Works.

5.21 SETTING MANHOLE COVERS AND FRAMES
1. Manhole frames shall be set to the required level on Class B engineering brickwork, or on precast concrete cover frame seating rings, as described in the Contract. The frames shall be set to level, bedded and haunched over the base and sides of the frame in Class M1 mortar.

5.22 CONNECTIONS TO EXISTING SEWERS
1. Pipe saddles for concrete or clay sewers shall be bedded in Class M1mortar and a mortar fillet formed to give a cover of at least 50 mm to the base of the saddle. Pipe saddles for asbestos-cement sewer pipes shall be formed from asbestos-cement and fixed with an epoxy resin adhesive.

2. Pipe saddles for uPVC pipes shall be purpose made from uPVC and shall either be of a mechanical clip-on type or shall be fixed with an appropriate solvent cement.

3. Where a connection without a saddle is to be made to an existing sewer, the pipes shall be splay cut to give an oblique junction, so that the discharge is in the direction of flow in the main sewer. The connecting pipes shall be of such a length that the socket of the cut pipe rests on the outside barrel of the sewer with no projection inside the main sewer. The pipe joint shall then be pointed in Class M1 mortar externally, and internally where practicable. Alternatively, purpose made junctions may be used by cutting out sections of pipe, fitting a junction and securing with repair couplings.

4. The ends of connections and pipes not required for immediate use shall be closed with purpose made stoppers, discs or joinders. The position of all junctions shall be recorded by the Contractor by measurement from the manhole immediately downstream and notified to the Engineer before backfilling is commenced.

5.23 SEWERS AND MANHOLES TO BE ABANDONED
1. Where sewers are to be abandoned and filled by grouting, the lowest point of the abandoned length shall be suitably sealed, and the filling operation shall commence from that point and continue progressively so as to fill all voids completely.

2. The shafts of manholes on abandoned sewers shall be broken down to a level 1 m below finished ground level and the remaining void filled as described in the Contract.

5.24 PIPE JACKING
1. Excavation for pipe jacking shall be undertaken from within a shield equipped with steering jacks for adjusting the alignment. Face boards shall be available for boarding up the exposed excavation.

2. The Contractor shall provide such continuous superintendence as is necessary to maintain the line and level during jacking of the pipe.

3. The Contractor shall limit the jacking load applied to the pipeline such that damage to the pipes is avoided and in this connection he shall be responsible for deciding whether an intermediate jacking station is needed.

(i) See also Clause 7.8.

(i) This clause covers the normal case. If bedding of frames on epoxy resin or haunching in concrete (instead of mortar) is required, this should be described in the Contract.

(i) For a review of practice and recommendations in making connections to pipe sewers, see Technical Paper No. 1 published by the WAA.

(i) The material required for filling should be described in the Contract.

(ii) Any requirement for clearing sewers prior to filling should be described in the Contract.

(i) Clause 15 of the Fifth Edition deals generally with superintendence; this clause ensures continuous superintendence during jacking operations.

(ii) Advice on intermediate jacking stations is given in 'A Guide to Pipe Jacking Design' published by the Pipe Jacking Association in June 1981.

4. The jacking load shall be transferred to the pipes through a thrust ring, which shall be sufficiently rigid to ensure even distribution of the load.

5. The pipe manufacturer's described permitted draw or angular deflection in relation to Table 6 of BS 5911: Part 120 shall not be exceeded at any individual joint.

6. The Contractor shall maintain up to date Site records of jacking loads and line and level measurements.

7. All lifting holes and grouting holes shall be sealed with Class M1 mortar.

8. Unless otherwise required by the Contract joint packing material designed to distribute the jacking load evenly shall be inserted at and between the pipe ends and at any intermediate jacking stations.

9. Where grouting is required this shall be carried out in accordance with Clause 5.30, after the pipes have been jacked into their final position.

5.25 SHAFTS

(iii) Collars fabricated from weldable structural steel may be susceptible to corrosion from the ground, ground water or the effluent carried. If corrosion can be expected, the design of joint should provide for a secondary sealing gasket to be applied on Site.

1. The Contractor shall provide temporary ladders to all shafts, with landings at intervals not exceeding 6 m. Protection shall be so provided that neither the ladders, landings, supporting structures nor persons using them are subject to the risk of damage or injury by the passage of skips and/or materials in the shaft.

(i) Any special requirements relating to protection should be described in the Contract.

2. Segments used in shafts shall be so erected as to break vertical joint except in any rings required to be broken out.

(ii) Special clauses will be required for other types of shaft sinking.

3. Where shafts are constructed by underpinning and lined with segments, they shall be grouted up at least once per shift.

4. After any primary lining is complete and before any openings are made at or near the foot, the excavation for the base of the shaft shall be taken out and the base concreted.

5.26 OPENINGS IN SHAFTS AND TUNNELS

(i) Although the Engineer may call for details under Clause 14(3) of the Fifth Edition, this clause is included to make the submission of details obligatory.

1. The Contractor shall supply to the Engineer drawings showing his proposals for forming openings in shafts and tunnels. These drawings shall include details of temporary supports to the lining and to the ground.

2. Openings in shafts and tunnels shall only be made after the segments have been grouted.

(ii) The Contract should describe any limitations which the design of the tunnel or shaft will impose on temporary openings.

5.27 SEGMENTAL SHAFT AND TUNNEL LININGS

1. Before each ring of any segmental lining is erected, any loose material or other obstructions shall be removed from any exposed Final Surface.

2. Segments shall be erected and assembled in-situ ring by ring and joint faces shall be clean on erection. The lining shall be built as soon as possible after the ground has been cut.

5.28 UNBOLTED CONCRETE TUNNEL SEGMENTS

(i) Requirements for any circumferential pre-stress should be described in the Contract.

1. The shape of unbolted concrete segmental tunnels shall be maintained within tolerance after erection, until the segments have been stabilised by grout or other means.

2. Where a circumferential pre-stress is applied, the force shall be such that the whole of the concrete lining is expanded tight against the surrounding ground. An approved graphite compound shall be applied to the wedge faces of segments immediately prior to expanding the ring.

3. Where wedge block segments are specified, the excavated tunnel periphery shall be lubricated to reduce skin friction.

4. Where key segments are shorter than other segments comprising the ring, the pockets formed shall be filled with Grade C20 concrete.

5.29 BOLTED CONCRETE SEGMENTAL LININGS

(i) Any requirement relating to rolling of segments should be described in the Contract.

1. Segmental joints to bolted concrete tunnel and shaft linings shall be trued and longitudinal joint bolts tightened before the final tightening of the circumferential joint bolts connecting the ring to the adjacent ring.

(ii) Any requirement for bituminous jointing strips in circumferential joints should be described in the Contract.

2. Bituminous jointing strip shall be provided to longitudinal joints.

3. Packings shall be inserted in the joints of the lining at the time of erection, as required, to maintain correct shape, line and level.

4. Two grummets shall be threaded on each bolt to be grummetted, at the time any bolted segment is erected. One grummet shall be placed under the washer at the head of the bolt and the other under the washer at the nut.

5.30 GROUTING OF SEGMENTS

(i) Any requirements for high pressure grouting should be described in the Contract.

1. Segmental shaft and tunnel linings shall be grouted by forcing the required grout through the grouting holes in the segments, so that all interstices around the outside of the segments are filled. Adequate venting shall be provided to ensure that air is not trapped. Grouting shall closely follow the erection of rings and shall be undertaken at least once per shift.

2. Temporary hardwood plugs shall be inserted into grout holes after grouting; these shall be replaced by permanent plugs of material similar to that of the segments being grouted when it is evident to the Engineer that grouting has been effective.

3. Grout pipes shall be provided in head walls or ring walls and any void remaining after concreting shall be filled with the required grout.

5.31 CAULKING

(i) Material to be used for caulking should be described in the Contract.

(ii) The time when caulking is carried out may depend, inter alia, upon ground conditions and availability of the working area.

1. Caulking of segment joints in tunnels and shafts shall be carried out as late as practicable within the construction programme; the grooves shall be raked out and cleaned immediately before caulking.

2. Caulking of circumferential and longitudinal joints shall be bonded to form a homogeneous and continuous mass consolidated to fill the recess up to the inner surface of the segment or to the depths described in the Contract.

5.32 POINTING OF JOINTS

1. Where joints between segments are required to be pointed, they shall be raked out, cleaned, filled with cement mortar Class M1 and pointed flush.

5.33 SHAFTS AND TUNNELS TO BE WATERTIGHT

(i) See also Clause 7.8.

1. Shafts and tunnels shall be substantially watertight, with no indentifiable flow of water penetrating either the primary or secondary lining.

5.34 RECORDING INFORMATION

1. The Contractor shall keep records of the line, level and the diameter measured horizontally and vertically of any tunnel lining and shall give copies of these records daily to the Engineer. Similar records shall be kept and supplied for shafts and for pipe jacking.

5.35 TOLERANCES FOR PIPELINES, SHAFTS AND TUNNELS

1. The position of the internal face of any pipeline, shaft or tunnel shall not deviate from that described in the Contract by more than the following permissible deviations:

Work category	Dimension or alignment	Permissible deviation
Pipeline	Line and level	20 mm
Pipe jacking	Line	75 mm
	Level	50 mm
Shafts and chambers	Vertically	1 in 300
Shafts and tunnels	Finished diameter	1% but not exceeding 50 mm
Tunnels without secondary lining	Line (shield drive)	75 mm
	Line (hand drive)	50 mm
	Level (shield drive)	50 mm
	Level (hand drive)	25 mm
Tunnels with secondary lining	Line	20 mm
	Level	10 mm
Shaft, tunnel and sewer lining segments	Maximum lipping between edges of adjacent segments	5 mm

ASSOCIATED TOPICS

1. Clauses relating to steel pipelines have been omitted because such projects are infrequent and because contract requirements will vary more than for most other pipe materials. General guidance on this topic may be obtained by reference to BS 2971, BS 4515, BS 5135, BS 534 and BS 3601.

SECTION 6

BUILDING WORKS

General Note

This Section is intended only for small scale building works to be carried out under the Fifth Edition of the ICE Conditions of Contract.

(i) Flush jointing is described in BS 5628: Part 3.

(ii) Any requirement for rendering of manholes and chambers should be described in the Contract.

(iii) The brickwork bond should be described in the Contract.

(iv) The required class of mortar and type of cement should be described in the Contract. See Clause 2.20.

6.1 BRICKWORK GENERALLY

1. Brickwork shall comply with the relevant provisions of BS 5628: Part 3.

2. The moisture content of the bricks shall be adjusted so that excessive suction is not exerted on the mortar.

3. Bricks in each course shall break joint correctly with the bricks underneath. The courses shall be laid parallel with joints of uniform thickness and shall be kept straight or regularly curved as required. Brickwork shall be gauged to rise 300 mm in four courses. Vertical joints shall be in alignment as required by the bond and shall have an average thickness of 10 mm. Bricks forming reveals and internal and external angles shall be selected for squareness and built plumb. Bricks with single frogs shall be laid frog upwards.

4. Brickwork shall rise uniformly; corners and other advanced work shall be racked back and not raised above the general level more than 1 m. No brickwork shall be carried up higher than 1.5 m in one day. No bats or broken bricks shall be incorporated in the work unless essential for bond.

5. Completed brickwork shall be protected at all times from scaffold splash, mortar droppings, grout leakage from suspended slabs and the harmful effects of weather. Brickwork shall be allowed to set thoroughly hard before cutting or chasing is carried out.

(i) The type of jointing and pointing should be described in the Contract.

(ii) Provision should be made in the Contract for sample areas of different wall types and finishes.

6.2 BRICKWORK, JOINTING AND POINTING

1. Bricks and blocks shall be laid in mortar properly bedded and jointed and all joints filled with mortar at every course.

2. Where the surface of walling does not provide an adequate key, the joints on faces of walls to be plastered shall be raked out 12 mm deep.

(i) Where the filling or semi-filling of cavities with insulating material is required it should be described in the Contract.

6.3 CAVITY WALLS

1. Cavity walls shall have 50 mm minimum width cavities and shall be built with wall ties uniformly spaced 450 mm apart vertically and 900 mm apart horizontally, staggered, and laid to fall outwards. Additional ties shall be used near the sides of all openings, one for each third course of bricks. Care shall be taken to keep the ties within the cavity free from mortar or mortar droppings and any mortar or debris collecting at the bottom of the cavity shall be cleaned out through temporary openings left for this purpose in the bottom courses.

6.4 DAMP PROOF COURSE

1. Construction of damp proof courses shall comply with the relevant provisions of CP 102: Section 3, BS 5628: Part 3 and BS 6576.

6.5 CORBELLING

1. Oversail corbelling shall not exceed 30 mm on each course.

6.6 BONDING TO CONCRETE

1. Where brickwork is to be bonded to concrete, this shall be achieved by means of metal ties evenly placed at three per square metre and brickwork shall be brought up subsequent to the concrete.

(i) Larger scale underpinning should be described in the Contract and may require the services of a specialist contractor.

6.7 UNDERPINNING

1. Underpinning in brickwork shall be carried up to within one course of the underside of the existing structure and allowed to set. The remaining course shall be bedded in mortar and wedged with slate pieces tightly against the existing structure.

6.8 CENTERING AND LAGGING

1. Centering and lagging used for the construction of brickwork shall remain in place for such time as is necessary for the brickwork to develop sufficient strength to prevent sagging or cracking of joints.

6.9 BRICKLAYING IN COLD WEATHER

1. Materials used in bricklaying shall be frost free and no bricks shall be laid when the ambient temperature is below 3°C, unless special precautions are taken. The Contractor shall ensure that any additive used in the mortar does not cause a variation in the colour of the joints. Completed work shall be protected adequately during cold weather.

6.10 PREPARATION FOR PLASTERING

1. Unless a bonding agent is used concrete ceilings, ceiling beams, columns and stanchions shall be dubbed out as necessary before plastering is commenced and the mix used for dubbing shall be similar to that used for first undercoating. The surface of in-situ concrete shall be cleaned of dust, loose particles and other matter. Surfaces shall be wetted immediately before plastering is commenced.

(i) The type of scrim material should be described in the Contract.

(ii) If joints are to be cut or covered as an alternative to scrim this should be described in the Contract.

2. Angles between walls and ceilings, vertical angles and joints between dissimilar solid backgrounds shall be reinforced with 90 mm wide scrim set in plaster and trowelled flat. All joints between plasterboards shall be similarly treated.

3. Expanded metal angle beads shall be provided at all external corners.

6.11 FIXING OF PLASTERBOARD

1. Plasterboard for ceilings shall be nailed to support at 150 mm centres with 40 mm sheradised plasterboard nails and fastened so that the joints are staggered. Noggins or other fixing surface shall be provided as necessary to ensure that edges of plasterboard are secured adequately. Ends of sheets shall be butted tightly and edges left with a gap not exceeding 5 mm.

2. Where sheeting has been cut, nails shall not be less than 18 mm from cut edges. Nails shall be driven well home with heads slightly below the surface, but shall not break the paper.

6.12 PLASTERING

1. Plastering shall normally be applied in two coats in accordance with the manufactuer's instructions and batches shall be used as soon as possible after water has been added. The total thickness of both coats shall be of the order of, but shall not exceed, 13 mm.

2. Where 3 coat work is described in the Contract, the thickness shall be of the order of, but shall not normally exceed, 18 mm.

3. The thickness of 2 coat work applied to concrete ceilings and soffits or plasterboard, shall not exceed 9 mm.

4. The thickness of finishing coats shall be of the order of 3 mm, except where board finished plaster is used, when the thickness shall be 5 mm and the work shall comply with the relevant provisions of BS 5492.

6.13 PLASTERING IN COLD WEATHER

1. When the ambient temperature is 5°C or less, the portion of the Works to be plastered shall be completely enclosed. The ambient temperature shall be raised and maintained above 5°C until the completion of plastering and hydration.

6.14 CONCRETE FLOOR FINISHES

1. Concrete floor finishes shall comply with the relevant provisions of BS 8204: Part 2.

(i) The type of finish from BS 8204: Part 2 should be described in the Contract.

6.15 FLOOR TILING

1. Floor tiling shall comply with the relevant provisions of CP 202 and BS 8203 for rigid and flexible tiling respectively.

6.16 TERAZZO

1. Terazzo floor finishes shall comply with the relevant provisions of CP 204: Section 3.

6.17 EXTERNAL RENDERING

1. External rendering shall comply with BS 5262 and shall be applied to a total thickness of not less than 20 mm. The mix for both coats shall be as for Class M4 mortar and the first coat shall be thrown on from a trowel, levelled with a straight edge, scratched and left to dry for not less than 3 days in warm weather and not less than 7 days in cold or wet weather. The suction of the surface of the first coat shall be adjusted as necessary by wetting before applying the second coat which shall be coloured as directed, levelled with a straight edge and lightly trowelled with a wooden trowel.

6.18 WALL TILING

1. Wall tiling shall comply with the relevant provisions of BS 5385: Parts 1, 2 and 4.

6.19 CARPENTRY AND JOINERY

1. Wherever possible, cutting and shaping of all timber shall be completed before preservative treatment is carried out. Where any cutting or shaping has to be carried out after treatment, the cut or worked surfaces shall be given 2 coats of the preservative. After treatment, timber shall be thoroughly dried out before use.

2. The whole of the joinery shall be cut and framed together as soon as possible after the commencement of the work. Workmanship shall comply with the relevant provisions of BS 1186: Part 2 and BS 6446. Except where work is described in the Contract as being to finished sizes, 3 mm shall be allowed for each wrot face. Frames, casings and other joinery fittings shall be secured to hardwood fixing slips built in for the purpose. Where hardwood fixing slips have not been provided, receiving surfaces shall be plugged with hardwood plugs or approved proprietary type plugs.

3. Manufactured units to be painted shall be primed at the place of manufacture.

6.20 STRUCTURAL STEELWORK

1. All steelwork shall be Grade 43A to BS 4360.

2. All members shall be cut to length by cold sawing.

3. Where a structural member is supported on masonry or brickwork, the minimum length of bearing shall be 100 mm.

(i) This clause is intended to apply to minor structural steel members.

(ii) End connection, baseplates and other design requirements should be described in the Contract.

(iii) Where steelwork is to be galvanised it should be described in the Contract.

(i) CP 112: Part 3 also covers the design of timber roofs.

6.21 ROOFS

1. Roof members shall be fabricated and erected in accordance with CP 112: Part 3.

2. Flats and gutters shall be covered with Type WBP plywood or tongued and grooved wrot boarding laid diagonally, firred to falls or not less than 1 in 120 for lead and copper and 1 in 60 for bitumen felt.

6.22 TIMBER FLOORS

1. Floor joists shall be either built into brickwork or blockwork, or held in galvanised steel joist hangers, and shall be trimmed as described in the Contract or as directed by the Engineer. Bridging shall be spaced at every 1.8 m apart and shall be 50 mm thick to the full depth of the joists or 38 mm by 50 mm herringbone strutting.

(i) Thickness of floor boarding should be described in the Contract.

(ii) If chipboard is to be used instead of floor boarding this should be described in the Contract.

2. Boarding shall be cramped up and nailed with cut flooring nails. Trimmed openings shall have mitred borders 75 mm in width.

6.23 DOOR FRAMES

1. Door frames shall be fitted into prepared openings, drilled and plugged at 3 points per jamb and shall have 100 mm by 12 mm diameter galvanised steel dowels to posts let into flooring and bedded in non-shrink or epoxy grout.

2. The joint between external door frames and adjacent walls shall be continuously pointed with gun applied butyl or other approved non-setting mastic.

6.24 WINDOWS

1. Window frames shall be securely fixed to openings in accordance with manufacturer's instructions and shall be continuously pointed with gun applied butyl or other approved non-setting mastic.

6.25 GLAZING

1. Glazing shall comply with the relevant provision of BS 6262.

(i) BS 6952: Part 1 gives guidance on exterior paint protection systems.

6.26 PAINTING

1. Painting of structural steelwork shall comply with the relevant provisions of BS 5493 and that of light steel sections used in buildings shall conform to the relevant recommendations of DD24. Other painting shall comply with the relevant provisions of BS 6150.

(i) The types and sizes of slate and tiles, together with details of any laps, battens, fixings, beddings, underfelt and boarding should be described in the Contract.

6.27 SLATING AND TILING

1. Slating and tiling work shall comply with the relevant provisions of BS 5534: Part 1.

6.28 LIGHTWEIGHT CONCRETE ROOF SCREEDS

1. Lightweight concrete roof screeds shall be laid to the necessary falls and shall comply with the relevant provisions of CP 144: Part 3. Before any felt is laid, a coat of bitumen primer shall be applied and allowed to dry.

(i) A written guarantee may be available for asphalt work incorporating terms currently applied by the Mastic Asphalt Council and Employers' Federation.

6.29 ASPHALT ROOFING

1. Mastic asphalt shall be laid in accordance with the relevant provisions of CP 144: Part 4 on an underlay of sheathing felt, laid loose and with joints lapped at least 50 mm. The roof shall be set out with properly formed high points, water lines and mitred bays where required.

6.30 BITUMEN FELT ROOFING
1. Built-up bitumen felt roof coverings shall be laid in accordance with the relevant provisions of CP 144: Part 3.

6.31 SURFACE TREATMENT TO FLAT ROOFS
(i) If reflective paint is to be used as an alternative to mineral aggregates, it should be described in the Contract.

1. Mineral aggregates for flat roofs shall be applied to flat asphalt and bitumen felt roofs where so described in the Contract.

6.32 PLUMBING
(i) Where heating and hot water systems are to be installed, reference should be made to BS 5449: Part 1 and BS 6880: Parts 1–3.

1. Plumbing for domestic water supply shall comply with the relevant provisions of BS 6700 and local water undertaking byelaws.

6.33 OPENINGS IN WALLS, FLOORS AND CEILINGS
1. The Contractor shall box out and/or cut openings through walls, floors and ceilings for the passage of pipes and cables and, where described in the Contract, shall provide and fix in position approved tube sleeves cut off flush with the finished surface. All openings and ducts shall be sealed on completion to prevent the passage of toxic or explosive gases.

6.34 TOLERANCES FOR BUILDING WORKS
1. Tolerances for building works, except where otherwise described in the Contract, shall not exceed the permissible deviations from levels and dimensions given in BS 5606, where applicable, for the corresponding types of work.

ASSOCIATED TOPICS

1. ELECTRICAL INSTALLATIONS
Domestic wiring and other electrical installations within buildings should comply with the Regulations for Electrical Installations, Fifteenth Edition published by the Institution of Electrical Engineers.

To enable the Contractor to comply with the IEE Regulations certain facts (e.g. the size of cables in the incoming supply) should be described in the Contract.

2. JOINTS IN BUILDINGS CONSTRUCTION
For guidance on the design of joints and jointing in building construction, see BS 6093.

TESTING AND STERILISATION

General Note

The action to be taken in the event of failure to satisfy the tests specified has only been referred to in general terms where the test so requires. See Clauses 36 and 39 of the Fifth Edition.

7.1 CLEANSING OF PIPELINES

1. On completion of construction, and before any sterilisation, internal surfaces of pipelines shall be cleaned thoroughly in such a way as to remove all oil, grit and other deleterious matter.

7.2 PRECAUTIONS PRIOR TO TESTING PIPELINES

(i) Testing against a closed valve should not be permitted if there is any other alternative.

(ii) See also Clauses 5.1 and 5.6.

1. Before testing any pipeline, the Contractor shall ensure that it is anchored adequately and that thrusts from bends, branch outlets or from the pipeline ends are transmitted to solid ground or to a suitable temporary anchorage.

2. Open ends shall be stopped with plugs, caps or blank flanges properly jointed.

7.3 NOTIFICATION OF TEST

1. The Contractor shall notify the Engineer at least one clear working day beforehand of his intention to test a section of pipeline.

7.4 TESTING GRAVITY PIPELINES

(i) The type of test (air, water, visual or CCTV) should be described in the Contract.

1. Gravity pipelines laid in open cut shall be tested after they are jointed and before any concreting or backfilling is commenced, other than such as may be necessary for structural stability whilst under test.

2. The pipelines shall be tested by means of an air or water test or by a visual or closed circuit television (CCTV) examination, in lengths determined by the course of construction, in accordance with a programme approved by the Engineer.

3. A further test shall be carried out after the backfilling is complete.

7.5 WATER TEST FOR GRAVITY PIPELINES

(i) This clause is consistent with the provisions of BS 8005: Part 1.

1. The test pressure for gravity pipelines up to and including 750 mm nominal bore shall be not less than 1.2 m head of water above the pipe soffit or ground water level, whichever is the higher at the highest point, and not greater than 6 m head at the lowest point of the section. Steeply graded pipelines shall be tested in stages in cases where the maximum head, as stated above, would be exceeded if the whole section were tested in one length.

2. The pipeline shall be filled with water and a minimum period of 2 hours shall be allowed for absorption, after which water shall be added from a measuring vessel at intervals of 5 minutes and the quantity required to maintain the original water level noted. Unless otherwise specified, the length of pipeline shall be accepted if the quantity of water added over a 30 minute period is less than 0.5 litre per lineal metre per metre of nominal bore.

7.6 AIR TEST FOR GRAVITY PIPELINES

(i) This clause is consistent with the provisions of BS 8005: Part 1.

1. Gravity pipelines to be air tested shall have air pumped in by suitable means until a pressure of 100 mm head of water is indicated in a U-tube connected to the system. The pipeline shall be accepted if the air pressure remains above 75 mm head of water after a period of 5 minutes without further pumping, following a period for stabilisation. Failure to pass the test shall not preclude acceptance of the pipeline if a successful water test, ordered by the Engineer, can subsequently be carried out in accordance with Clause 7.5.

7.7 CCTV INSPECTION OF PIPELINES

(i) CCTV inspection should be described in the Contract if required.

1. Where internal inspection of pipelines by CCTV is required, the Contractor shall provide all necessary equipment, including suitable covered accommodation for viewing the monitor screen, together with personnel experienced in the operation of the equipment and interpretation of results.

2. The intensity of illumination within the pipe and the rate of draw of the camera shall be such as to allow a proper examination of the inside of the pipe. Provision shall be made for the movement of the camera to be stopped and its position recorded and for permanent photographs to be taken at any point requested by the Engineer.

7.8 INFILTRATION

(i) The permissible infiltration is the same as the permissible loss in the water test in Clause 7.5.

1. Gravity pipelines (including tunnels) and manholes shall be tested for infiltration after backfilling. All inlets to the system shall be effectively closed, and any residual flow shall be deemed to be infiltration.

2. The pipeline, including manholes, shall be accepted as satisfactory if the infiltration, including infiltration into manholes, in 30 minutes does not exceed 0.5 litre per lineal metre per metre of nominal bore.

3. Notwithstanding the satisfactory completion of the above test, if there is any discernible flow of water entering the pipeline at a point which can be located either by visual or CCTV inspection, the Contractor shall take such measures as are necessary to stop such infiltration.

7.9 TESTING OF PRESSURE PIPELINES

(i) This clause is intended for application to pressure pipeline materials such as Ductile Iron, Asbestos-cement, GRP and uPVC. Where pipes are of MDPE, pre-stressed concrete, or other materials, special clauses will be necessary.

(ii) A large diameter pressure gauge has been specified to enable a small change in pressure to be accurately measured.

(iii) The standing period referred to in sub-clause 2 is to allow for absorption into concrete or other internal lining material. This period should be described in the Contract together with the design operating pressure.

(iv) The test pressures should be described in the Contract.

1. Gauges used for testing pressure pipelines shall either be of the conventional circular type, not less than 200 mm diameter, calibrated in metres head water, or shall have a digital indicator capable of reading increments of 0.1 m head. Before any gauge is used, the Contractor shall arrange for it to be checked independently and a dated certificate of its accuracy shall be provided.

2. Before testing, valves shall be checked and sealed, the sections of main filled with water and the air released. After having been filled, pipelines shall be left under operating pressure for the period described in the Contract, so as to achieve conditions as stable as possible for testing.

3. The pressure in the pipeline shall then be raised steadily until the specified test pressure is reached in the lowest part of the section, and the pressure shall be maintained at this level, by pumping if necessary, for a period of one hour. The pump shall then be disconnected, and no further water shall be permitted to enter the pipeline for a further period of one hour. At the end of this period the original pressure shall be restored by pumping and the loss measured by drawing off water from the pipeline until the pressure as at the end of the test is again reached.

4. The permissible loss shall not exceed 2 litres per metre nominal bore per kilometre length per metre head (calculated as the average head applied to the section) per 24 hours.

5. In addition to the tests on separate sections, the whole pipeline shall be tested on completion to the same pressure and by the same procedures as that outlined for individual sections.

6. Where a new pipeline is to connect to an operational pipeline the final connection shall be inspected visually under normal operating pressure and there shall be no visible leakage.

7.10 SWABBING OF WATER MAINS

(i) The Contract should describe who provides swabs and temporary pipework, the type of swab and the maximum number of passes to be run at the Employer's expense.

1. On completion of the hydraulic test on water mains, a foam swab shall be passed through the main for final cleansing, sufficient times to achieve clear wash water.

7.11 STERILISATION OF WATER MAINS

(i) If the Contractor is to be required to sterilise water mains, this should be described in the Contract.

1. Sterilisation and bacteriological sampling of completed sections of water mains shall be carried out by the Employer. Thereafter, the main shall be regarded as operational and the Contractor shall not turn any valves or take any other action which might interfere with the use of the main.

7.12 CLEANSING OF STRUCTURES

(i) This clause deals only with structures designed to retain an aqueous liquid. For cleansing of other structures, see Clause 33 of the Fifth Edition.

1. On completion of construction, and before any sterilisation, internal surfaces of structures designed to retain an aqueous liquid shall be cleaned thoroughly in such a way as to remove all oil, grit and other deleterious matter.

7.13 TESTING OF CONCRETE STRUCTURES DESIGNED TO RETAIN AN AQUEOUS LIQUID

(i) This clause is consistent with the recommendations of Clause 9.2 of BS 8007.

(ii) The 21 day stabilisation period is consistent with a design crack width of 0.2 mm or greater. The stabilisation period may be reduced to 7 days for maximum design crack width of 0.1 mm.

(iii) Clause 9.2 of BS 8007 gives guidance on retesting procedures.

1. After cleaning, and as far as practicable before any earth or other filling is placed against the outside wall faces, concrete structures designed to retain an aqueous liquid shall be filled with water at a uniform rate of not greater than 2m in 24 hours. A period of 21 days shall be allowed for stabilisation, after which the water level shall be recorded by a hook gauge with vernier attachment or by other approved means at 24 hour intervals for a test period of 7 days. During the test period the total permissible drop, after allowing for evaporation and rainfall, shall not exceed 1/500 of the average water depth of the full tank or 10 mm, whichever is the less.

2. Notwithstanding the satisfactory completion of the above test, any leakage visible on the outside faces of the structure shall be stopped. Any caulking or making good of cracks in the wall section shall, where practicable, be carried out from the inside face.

7.14 TESTING OF ROOFS

(i) The Contract should describe which of the two alternative tests is required.

(ii) This clause is consistent with the recommendations of Clause 9.3 of BS 8007, which gives guidance on retesting procedures.

1. Roofs of service reservoirs shall be watertight and shall, where practicable, be tested on completion by lagooning with water to a minimum depth of 25 mm for a period of 24 hours.

2. Where it is impracticable, because of roof falls or otherwise, to contain 25 mm depth of water, the roof shall be thoroughly wetted by continuous hosing for a period of not less than 6 hours.

3. In either case, the roof shall be regarded as satisfactory if no leaks or damp patches show in the soffit.

4. The roof covering shall be completed as soon as possible after satisfactory testing.

7.15 STERILISATION OF STRUCTURES FOR POTABLE WATER

(i) This clause will not apply if the Employer wishes to undertake sterilisation.

(ii) For provisions relating to pollution of watercourses, see Clause 1.14.

1. Immediately before acceptance of any structure for potable water, the interior shall be sterilised using water chlorinated to give a residual of not less than 20 mg/l of free chlorine. The structure shall be emptied, flushed with mains water and then filled with water having a chlorine residual or not more than 0.5 mg/l free chlorine to normal top water level.

2. After 24 hours the Engineer shall arrange for a sample to be taken for bacteriological analysis. The structure shall be deemed to be sterile if there are no coliforms in the sample. If there are coliforms in the sample the Engineer shall arrange for one further sample to be taken and the structure shall be deemed to be sterile if there are no coliforms in that sample.

7.16 TESTING OF GROUT STRENGTH

(i) Requirements for grout testing should be described in the Contract.

1. Cube moulds shall be 70 mm (nominal) or 100 mm and all joints shall be sealed to prevent leakage.

2. Moulds shall be overfilled and air bubbles removed by lightly tapping the mould. After leaving for 30 – 60 minutes the excess grout shall be struck off and the moulds covered with plastic sheeting or damp hessian. Moulds shall be stored at 20°C ±5°C for 24 hours, or until the grout has attained sufficient strength to allow the cube to be stripped from the mould, whichever is the greater.

3. The cubes shall be removed from the moulds, marked and stored in water at a temperature of 20°C ±1°C until tested.

4. Cubes shall be tested 28 days after casting.

ASSOCIATED TOPICS

1.   Testing of Operational Equipment
Testing of operational equipment installed by the Contractor should be described in item descriptions (CESMM Class A.2.6).

2.   Provision of Water for Testing
The Contract should describe who is responsible for providing water for each testing operation and for disposing of test water on completion, having regard to the pollution of watercourses. See Clause 1.14.

General Note

This Section is not intended to cover the construction of prospectively adoptable highways but, together with the relevant materials clauses, is based generally on the requirements of the Department of Transport's Specification for Highway Works; abbreviated and simplified to take account of the type of road normally required in association with water industry work.

(i) A described cross-section of the carriageway construction, and the position and type of any joints, should be described in the Contract.

8.1   ROAD FORMATIONS

1. The road formation shall be the surface obtained after completion of any earthworks.

2. Formations, immediately before being covered with sub-base or road base material, shall be clean, free from mud and slurry and properly shaped and compacted to an even and uniform surface.

3. The preparation and surface treatment of formations shall be carried out after the reinstatement of any excavations for services.

(i) If a lean-mix concrete sub-base is required, this should be described in the Contract.

8.2   SUB-BASE CONSTRUCTION

1. Within 48 hours of completion of a road formation, granular sub-base material shall be spread and compacted to the required thickness. The sub-base shall be protected from deterioration due to ingress of water, the adverse effects of weather and the use of Constructional Plant. Compaction shall be carried out in accordance with the following table:

Type of compaction plant	Category	Number of passes for layers not greater than:		
		110 mm	150 mm	225 mm
Smooth-wheeled roller	Mass per metre width of roll:			
	over 2700 kg up to 5400 kg	16	unsuitable	unsuitable
	over 5400 kg	8	16	unsuitable
Pneumatic-tyred roller	Mass per wheel:			
	over 4000 kg up to 6000 kg	12	unsuitable	unsuitable
	over 6000 kg up to 8000 kg	12	unsuitable	unsuitable
	over 8000 kg up to 12000 kg	10	16	unsuitable
	over 12000 kg	8	12	unsuitable
Vibrating roller	Mass per metre width of vibrating roll:			
	over 700 kg up to 1300 kg	16	unsuitable	unsuitable
	over 1300 kg up to 1800 kg	6	16	unsuitable
	over 1800 kg up to 2300 kg	4	6	10
	over 2300 kg up to 2900 kg	3	5	9
	over 2900 kg up to 3600 kg	3	5	8
	over 3600 kg up to 4300 kg	2	4	7
	over 4300 kg up to 5000 kg	2	4	6
	over 5000 kg	2	3	5
Vibrating-plate compactor	Mass per unit area of base plate:			
	over 1400 kg/m² up to 1800 kg/m²	8	unsuitable	unsuitable
	over 1800 kg/m² up to 2100 kg/m²	5	8	unsuitable
	over 2100 kg/m²	3	6	10
Vibro-tamper	Mass:			
	over 50 kg up to 65 kg	4	8	unsuitable
	over 65 kg up to 75 kg	3	6	10
	over 75 kg	2	4	8
Power rammer	Mass:			
	100 kg – 500 kg	5	8	unsuitable
	over 500 kg	5	8	12

8.3 WET-MIX MACADAM CONSTRUCTION

1. Wet-mix macadam shall be spread evenly on the sub-base and compacted in layers of not more than 200 mm thickness at the optimum moisture content ±0.5%.

2. Spreading shall be undertaken concurrently with placing. Compaction shall be completed as soon as possible after the material has been spread and carried out in accordance with the table in Clause 8.2.

8.4 LEAN CONCRETE CONSTRUCTION

1. Lean concrete construction for roads shall be Grade C7.5 and shall be spread evenly on the sub-base and laid and compacted in layers of not more than 200 mm thickness.

2. Spreading shall be undertaken concurrently with placing. Compaction shall be completed as soon as possible after the material has been spread and carried out in accordance with the table in Clause 8.2. The maximum period of time between mixing of the materials and final compacting of any given material shall be 2 hours.

3. Where practicable, joints against hardened material shall be avoided. Where such joints are unavoidable, the hardened material shall be cut back vertically for the full depth of the layer before placing any further adjacent material.

4. Lean concrete shall be cured for a period of not less than 7 days. No vehicular traffic shall be allowed to run on the base during this time.

8.5 LAYING COATED MACADAM

(i) BS 4987 covers the laying of macadam carriageways, footways and other lightly trafficked areas.

1. Transportation, laying and compaction of all coated macadam shall be carried out in accordance with the relevant provisions of BS 4987.

8.6 LAYING HOT ROLLED ASPHALT

1. Transportation, laying and compaction of hot rolled asphalt shall be carried out in accordance with the relevant provisions of BS 594: Part 2.

8.7 WATERPROOF UNDERLAY FOR CONCRETE CARRIAGEWAYS

1. Waterproof underlay shall consist of waterproof paper or impermeable plastic sheeting, laid to provide a membrane immediately below the concrete. Overlaps shall be not less than 300 mm and precautions shall be taken to prevent ponding on the membrane.

8.8 REINFORCEMENT OF CONCRETE CARRIAGEWAYS

(i) This clause assumes that only a single layer of reinforcement is necssary.

1. Reinforcement in concrete carriageways shall be so placed that, after compaction of the concrete, its cover below the finished surface of the slab is 60 mm (±10 mm) and it terminates 125 mm (±25 mm) from the edges of the slab and all pre-formed joints in the concrete.

2. At transverse joints between mats of steel fabric reinforcement, the longitudinal bars shall overlap by at least 35 times the bar diameter, provided that such overlap shall not in any case be less than 450 mm. Mats shall be placed so as to maintain the same spacing between edge longitudinal bars as in the body of the mat.

3. Reinforcement shall be positioned above dowel bars and tie bars irrespective of the tolerances on position.

8.9 LAYING CONCRETE CARRIAGEWAYS

(i) The positioning and detailing of movement joints should be described in the Contract.

1. Placing, compacting and finishing of concrete in carriageways shall be carried out in one layer as rapidly as possible and shall be so arranged that, in any transverse section, the time for completion of mixing the first batch of concrete to completion of compaction of that section shall not exceed 2 hours.

2. Carriageway surfaces shall have a Screeded Finish, which shall be brushed transversely with a medium textured wire broom to produce a lightly brushmarked finish, with a 100 mm arris Steel Trowel Finish to sides and at joints.

3. Surface irregularities shall not exceed 3 mm when checked with a 3 m straight edge.

8.10 LAYING KERBS AND CHANNELS

(i) Details of the concrete bed and haunch should be described in the Contract.

1. Kerbs, edgings, channels and quadrants shall be laid and bedded on a layer of Class M1 mortar, either on the concrete carriageway or on a Grade C20 concrete foundation, as described in the Contract. They shall be butt-jointed except where otherwise described in the Contract, save that where laid on concrete carriageways they shall be provided with joints coincident with the carriageway movement joints, of width and with filler identical to that used in the carriageway joints. All kerbs shall be backed with Grade C20 concrete.

2. For radii of 12 m or less, kerbs and channels of the appropriate radius shall be used.

3. Alignment of kerbs and channels shall not deivate from that described in the Contract by more than 10 mm, with no lipping of visible faces.

8.11 FOUNDATIONS FOR FOOTWAYS

(i) A described cross-section of the footway construction should be described in the Contract.

1. Foundations for footways shall consist of Type 1 granular sub-base material spread evenly and compacted in layers of not more than 100 mm thickness.

2. Compaction to the correct levels shall be carried out using a vibratory roller having a static load of at least 1000 kg/m width of roll.

8.12 LAYING CONCRETE PAVING FLAGS

1. Precast concrete flags shall be laid to the required falls on sub-base material as described in the Contract, bonded with joints at right angles to the kerb, and spot bedded with Class M4 mortar with no lipping of top surfaces.

2. Flags shall be cut to fit around surface boxes and other furniture and, on circular work where the radius is 12m or less, shall be radially cut on both edges to the required lines.

8.13 TOLERANCES FOR FINISHED CARRIAGEWAY SURFACES

1. Finished surfaces at each stage of road construction shall not vary from the levels described in the Contract by more than the following permissible deviations:

Surface	Permissible deviation (mm)
Formation and sub-base	+10, −30
Base	±15
Wearing surface or slab surface	± 6

2. The combination of permitted tolerances in the levels of different pavement courses shall not result in a reduction in thickness of the pavement, excluding the sub-base, by more than 15 mm from the specified thickness, nor a reduction in the thickness of the bituminous wearing course by more than 5 mm from that specified, and the maximum allowable irregularity of the wearing surface below a 3 m straight edge shall be 3 mm.

8.14 FIXING OF GULLIES

1. Gullies shall be bedded and surrounded with Grade C20 concrete to the thickness described in the Contract.

2. Frames shall be bedded in Class M1 mortar on two courses of Class 'B' engineering brickwork or precast concrete gully cover slabs.

SECTION 9

SEWER RENOVATION

General Note

This Section covers the fundamental requirements of sewer renovation works to be carried out under the Fifth Edition of the ICE Conditions of Contract and is based on the recommendations of the WAA/WRc Sewerage Rehabilitation Manual (Second Edition), 1986 (SRM).

Special Specification Clauses will normally be required to describe the particular renovation system required, whether or not a proprietary system is to be used.

Whenever a proprietary renovation system is offered, a described methods statement should be called for and its suitability assessed **before** acceptance of the tender. Guidance on the assessment of renovation systems is given in Chapters 7 and 8 and Appendix E of Volume 3 of the Sewerage Rehabilitation Manual.

The Contract should expressly provide that the Employer is not responsible for the methods of construction. Express provision should also be made where the Contractor is responsible for the design or specification of any part of the Permanent Works.

(i) See 1.AT.14 of Section 1.

(ii) Example flow schedules are given in the SRM.

9.1 SEWER FLOWS
1. The Contractor shall keep the working area free of flows unless otherwise described in the Contract.

9.2 PREPARATION OF EXISTING SEWERS
1. Sewers to be renovated shall be prepared so that the installation and performance of the renovation system is not impaired.

2. The Contractor shall take all precautions necessary to prevent debris being carried downstream whilst preparing or working in existing sewers.

9.3 COMMENCEMENT OF RENOVATION
1. The Contractor shall give adequate notice to the Engineer of his intention to commence renovation.

9.4 INTERNAL REPAIRS
1. The Contractor shall not jeopardise the stability of existing sewers whilst carrying out local internal repairs or stabilisation.

9.5 SURVEY OF EXISTING SEWERS
1. The Contractor shall carry out a survey of the sewers to be renovated and shall note the position, size and angle of approach of all laterals, to an accuracy appropriate to the method of reconnection.

9.6 JOINTING GENERALLY
1. Jointing surfaces and components shall be kept clean and free from extraneous matter until the joints have been made or assembled.

9.7 JOINTING OF GUNITE SEGMENTS
1. Joints between precast gunite lining segments shall be made in accordance with the relevant provisions of WIs No. 4-12-05.

2. Finished joints shall be free from dry patches, voids, sand pockets or sagged or slumped materials.

9.8 LATERALS
1. All laterals shall be reconnected and any circumferential lining joints shall not be made at or within 100 mm of a connection.

2. Each finished connection shall be made flush with the lined sewer and shall provide a smooth transition to the existing lateral pipework.

3. No connection shall be made to a polyethylene sliplining until the latter has relaxed sufficiently to prevent damage.

9.9 CUTTING OF LININGS

(i) Manufacturers of GRP linings give recommendations for the protection of cut edges. See also Clause 2.3.

1. Linings shall be cut in such a way as to avoid damage.

9.10 TREATMENT AT INTERMEDIATE MANHOLES

1. The Contractor shall ensure that at intermediate manholes the edges of the lining are adequately sealed and the benching made good.

9.11 RELEASE OF CURING WATER

1. Whenever hot water curing of a sewer lining is carried out the water shall not be released until it cools below 40°C.

9.12 ANNULUS GROUTING GENERALLY

1. All air, water and contaminated grout is to be expelled from the annulus by the grouting process.

2. The grout injection pressure shall be continuously measured by a suitable gauge fitted at the injection nozzle and shall not exceed 50 kN/m^2.

3. The quantity of grout injected at each injection point and the maximum pressure at the nozzle at that point shall be recorded and the records made available to the Engineer.

4. Segregation of the grout shall not take place during pumping operations.

9.13 GROUT QUALITY CONTROL TESTS

(i) Grout strength requirements should be described in the Contract.

1. Where tests are required for different properties of the grout, they shall be carried out on samples from the same batch.

2. The density and workability of every batch shall be determined. The density shall not differ from the value described in the Contract by more than 5%. The workability shall not differ by more than 125 mm for the 'Colcrete flow trough test' or 5 seconds for the 'Marsh cone test' with 10 mm orifice from the values described in the Contract.

3. Grout strength tests shall be carried out in accordance with Clause 7.16. Sampling shall be at the rate of 3 cubes taken from every 5 m^3 of grout or 50 m of grout annulus, whichever is the smaller. When tested in accordance with the relevant provisions of BS 4551, cubes shall have a compressive strength as given in the following table:

Grout function	Minimum compressive strength at 28 days (N/mm^2)
Annulus filling: Type I lining Type II lining	 12 3
Exterior void filling	2

9.14 INSPECTION AFTER GROUTING

1. Immediately after each grouting operation the Contractor shall inspect the sewer and any laterals and clean out any excess grout.

9.15 INSPECTION AFTER LINING OF NON MAN ENTRY SYSTEMS

(i) The format of the information required should be described in the Contract.

1. On completion of the Works the Contractor shall undertake a CCTV survey and provide the Engineer with a video recording of that survey.

APPENDIX I

INCORPORATION OF SPECIFICATION INTO CONTRACTS

It is not necessary to bind copies of the Civil Engineering Specification for the Water Industry, 3rd Edition, into the documents prepared for tenderers or into any formally sealed contract.

The Specification should be incorporated by reference by including the following provisions, in tender documents, immediately preceding the Special Specification Clauses:

SPECIFICATION

1. The Specification referred to in the Tender shall be the 'Civil Engineering Specification for the Water Industry, 3rd Edition', published by the Water Authorities Association in May 1989.

2. In so far as any Special Clause may conflict or be inconsistent with any provision of the Civil Engineering Specification for the Water Industry, 3rd Edition, the Special Clause shall always prevail.

Supplementary Clauses should be included in the Contract documents and numbered in two separate groups as follows:

(a) Specification requirements which are related to an existing clause should be numbered as additional sub-clauses (e.g. requirements for special flanges other than to BS 4504 should be numbered 2.47.2).

(b) New clauses unrelated to existing clauses should be numbered to follow the last clause of the appropriate Section.

APPENDIX II

List of British Standard Specifications to which reference is made in the document

BS	TITLE	REFERENCE(S)
4	Structural steel sections	
	Part 1: Hot rolled sections	2.68.1
12	Portland cement	2.15.1, 2.15.3, 2.15(vii), 4.15.1
*65	Vitrified clay pipes, fittings, joints and ducts	2.27.1, 2.27.2, 2.43.1, 2.44.2, 2.59.2
146	Portland-blastfurnace cements	
	Part 2: Metric Units	2.15.1, 2.15(iv)
187	Calcium silicate (sandlime and flintlime) bricks	2.105.1
340	Precast concrete kerbs, channels, edgings and quadrants	2.114.1
368	Precast concrete flags	2.115.1
402	Clay plain roofing tiles and fittings	2.102.1
*410	Test sieves	2.117.1, 2.118.1
*416	Cast iron spigot and socket soil, waste and ventilating pipes (sand cast and spun) and fittings	2.39.1
417	Galvanized mild steel cisterns and covers, tanks and cylinders	
	Part 2: Metric Units	2.40.1
434	Bitumen road emulsions (anionic and cationic)	
	Part 1: Bitumen road emulsions	2.121.1
435	Dressed natural stone kerbs, channels, quadrants and setts	2.111.1
459	Matchboarded wooden door leaves for external use	2.88.1
460	Cast iron rainwater goods	2.38.1
*473 & 550	Concrete roofing tiles and fittings	2.102.1
486	Asbestos-cement pressure pipes and joints	2.33.2
493	Airbricks and gratings for wall ventilation	2.105.4, 2.105(iii)
497	Manhole covers, road gully gratings and frames for drainage purposes	
	*Part 1: Cast iron and cast steel	2.57.1, 2.60.1
534	Steel pipes and specials for water and sewage	5.AT.1
544	Linseed oil putty for use in wooden frames	2.93.1
569	Asbestos-cement rainwater goods	2.38.1
584	Wood trim (softwood)	2.86.1, 2.86(i)
594	Hot rolled asphalt for roads and other paved areas	
	Part 1: Constituent materials and asphalt mixtures	2.120.1
	Part 2: Transport, laying and compaction of rolled asphalt	3.8.4, 3.8.5, 8.6.1
639	Covered carbon and carbon manganese steel electrodes for manual metal-arc welding	2.71.2
680	Roofing slates	
	Part 2: Metric Units	2.102.1
690	Asbestos-cement slates and sheets	
	Part 2: Asbestos-cement and cellulose-asbestos-cement flat sheets	2.102.1
	Part 4: Slates	2.102.1
	Part 5: Lining sheets and panels	2.102.1
729	Hot dip galvanized coatings on iron and steel articles	2.73.1, 2.74.2, 2.75.2, 2.76.2, 2.77.1, 2.77.2, 2.108.3, 2.109.3
*743	Materials for damp proof courses. Metric Units	2.52.2, 2.127(i)
747	Roofing felts	2.102.1
*750	Underground fire hydrants and surface box frames and covers	2.61.1

BS	TITLE	REFERENCE(S)
812	Testing aggregates	
	Part 2: Physical properties	2.10.3
	Part 3: Mechanical properties	2.117.5
	Part 103: Methods for determination of particle size distribution	2.117.4, 2.118.2
	Part 105: Methods for determination of particle shape	2.118.3
864	Capillary and compression tube fittings of copper and copper alloy	
	*Part 2: Capillary and compression fittings for copper tubes	2.40.1
877	Foamed or expanded blast-furnace slag lightweight aggregate for concrete	2.10.1, 2.10.2
882	Aggregates from natural sources for concrete (including granolithic)	2.10.1, 2.10.2, 2.11.1, 2.12.2, 2.12.4, 2.50.2, 4.6.1
890	Building limes	2.17.1
903	Methods of testing vulcanized rubber	
	Part A1: Determination of density	2.126.2
	Part A2: Determination of tensile stress-strain properties	2.126.2
	Part A3: Determination of tear strength (trouser, angle and crescent test piece)	2.126.2
	Part A16: Determination of the effect of liquids	2.126.2
	Part A26: Determination of hardness	2.126.2
	Part A36: Preparation of samples and test pieces	2.126.2
	Part A38: Determination of dimensions of test pieces and products for test purposes	2.126.2
952	Glass for glazing	
	Part 1: Classification	2.92.1
	Part 2: Terminology for work on glass	2.92(i)
970	Wrought steels for mechanical and allied engineering purposes	
	Part 1: General inspection and testing procedures and specific requirements for carbon, carbon manganese and stainless steels	2.72.4, 2.73.2, 2.74.1, 2.75.3, 2.77.1, 2.77.2
1010	Draw-off taps and stop valves for water services (screwdown pattern)	
	*Part 2: Draw-off taps and above ground stopvalves	2.40.1
1014	Pigments for Portland cement and Portland cement products	2.15.3
1047	Air-cooled blastfurnace slag aggregate for use in construction	2.10.1, 2.10.2
1052	Mild steel wire for general engineering purposes	2.22.1
1070	Black paint (tar-based)	2.69.3
*1125	WC flushing cisterns (including dual flush cisterns and flush pipes)	2.40.1
1142	Fibre building boards	
	Part 2: Medium board and hardboard	2.98.1
	Part 3: Insulating board (softboard)	2.52.1, 2.52(i), 2.98.1
1161	Aluminium alloy sections for structural purposes	2.70.1
1165	Clinker and furnace bottom ash aggregates for concrete	2.10.1, 2.10.2
1178	Milled lead sheet for building purposes	2.67.1, 2.104.1
1186	Quality of timber and workmanship in joinery	
	Part 1: Timber	2.85.1
	Part 2: Quality of workmanship	6.19.2
1188	Ceramic wash basins and pedestals	2.40.1
1191	Gypsum building plasters	
	Part 2: Premixed lightweight plasters	2.95.1, 2.95.2
*1194	Concrete porous pipes for under-drainage	2.43.1
1196	Clayware field drain pipes	2.43.1
1197	Concrete flooring tiles and fittings	
	Part 2: Metric Units	2.100.1

BS	TITLE	REFERENCE(S)
1199, 1200	Building sands from natural sources	2.12.1, 2.12.3, 2.12.4
1202	Nails	
	Part 1: Steel nails	2.79.1
	Part 2: Copper nails	2.79.1
	Part 3: Aluminium nails	2.79.1
1203	Synthetic resin adesives (phenolic and aminoplastic) for plywood	2.82.1
1204	Synthetic resin adhesives (phenolic and aminoplastic) for wood	2.82.1
1206	Fireclay sinks. Dimensions and workmanship	2.40.1
1212	Float operated valves (excluding floats)	
	*Part 2: Diaphragm type (brass body)	2.40.1
	*Part 3: Diaphragm type (plastics body) for cold water services	2.40.1
1217	Cast stone	2.112.1
1230	Gypsum plasterboard	
	Part 1: Plasterboard excluding materials submitted to secondary operations	2.98.1
1243	Metal ties for cavity wall construction	2.106.1
1244	Metal sinks for domestic purposes	
	*Part 2: Sit-on and inset sinks	2.40.1
*1247	Manhole step irons	2.58.1
*1254	WC seats (plastics)	2.40.1
1285	Wood surrounds for steel windows and doors	2.90.1
1297	Tongued and grooved softwood flooring	2.87.1
1329	Metal hand rinse basins	2.40.1
1336	Knotting	2.94.3
1369	Steel lathing for internal plastering and external rendering	
	Part 1: Expanded metal and ribbed lathing	2.96.1
1370	Low heat Portland cement	2.15.1
1377	Methods of test for soil for civil engineering purposes	2.14.3, 2.117.4
1387	Screwed and socketed steel tubes and tubulars and plain end steel tubes suitable for welding or for screwing to BS21 pipe threads	2.74.1
1438	Media for biological percolating filters	2.18.1, 2.18(ii), 2.18(iii)
1449	Steel plate, sheet and strip	
	Part 2: Stainless and heat-resisting steel plate, sheet and strip	2.72.4, 2.75.3, 2.77.1, 2.77.2
1470	Wrought aluminium and aluminium alloys for general engineering purposes—plate, sheet and strip	2.70.1
1471	Wrought aluminium and aluminium alloys for general engineering purposes—drawn tube	2.70.1, 2.74.1
1474	Wrought aluminium and aluminium alloys for general engineering purposes—bars, extruded round tubes and sections	2.70.1, 2.74.1, 2.75.4
1490	Aluminium and aluminium alloy ingots and castings for general engineering purposes	2.70.1, 2.74.1
1494	Fixing accessories for building purposes	
	Part 1: Fixings for sheet, roof and wall coverings	2.78.1
1521	Waterproof building papers	2.25.1
1567	Wood door frames and linings	2.88.1, 2.88(ii)
1579	Connectors for timber	2.80.1
1615	Method for specifying anodic oxidation coatings on aluminium and its alloys	2.74.2, 2.75.5
1706	Electroplated coatings of cadmium and zinc on iron and steel	2.77.2
1710	Identification of pipelines and services	2.44(ii)
1722	Fences	2.107.1, 2.107.2, 2.107(i)
1876	Automatic flushing cisterns for urinals	2.40.1

BS	TITLE	REFERENCE(S)
1968	Floats for ballvalves (copper)	2.40.1
*2456	Floats (plastics) for ballvalves for hot and cold water	2.40.1
*2494	Elastomeric joint rings for pipework and pipelines	2.46.1, 2.48.1
2499	Hot applied joint sealants for concrete pavements	2.125.2, 2.125(i)
2523	Lead-based priming paints	2.94.6
*2592	Thermoplastic flooring tiles	2.100.1
2789	Spheroidal graphite or nodular graphite cast iron	2.72.2
2871	Copper and copper alloys. Tubes	
	*Part 1: Copper tubes for water, gas and sanitation	2.40.1
*2879	Draining taps (screw-down pattern)	2.40.1
2901	Filler rods and wires for gas-shielded arc welding	
	Part 1: Ferritic steels	2.71.4
	Part 2: Austenitic stainless steels	2.71.4
	Part 4: Aluminium and aluminium alloys and magnesium alloys	2.71.4
2926	Chromium and chromium-nickel steel electrodes for manual metal-arc welding	2.71.2
2971	Class II arc welding of carbon steel pipework for carrying fluids	5.AT.1
2994	Cold rolled steel sections	2.68.1
2997	Aluminium rainwater goods	2.38.1
3019	TIG welding	
	Part 2: Austenitic stainless and heat-resisting steels	2.71(i)
3148	Water for making concrete (including notes on the suitability of the water)	2.9(ii)
3251	Indicator plates for fire hydrants and emergency water supplies	2.61.3
3260	Semi-flexible PVC floor tiles	2.100.1
3261	Unbacked flexible PVC flooring	
	Part 1: Homogeneous flooring	2.100.1
3380	Wastes for sanitary appliances and overflows for baths	2.39.2
3382	Electroplated coatings on threaded components	
	Part 1: Cadmium on steel components	2.77.2
	Part 2: Zinc on steel components	2.77.2
3416 & 6949	Bitumen-based coatings for cold application, suitable for use in contact with potable water	2.69.3
3470	Field gates and posts	2.108.1, 2.108.2
*3505	Unplasticized polyvinyl chloride (PVC-U) pressure pipe for cold potable water	2.32.1, 2.32.2, 2.40.1, 2.44.1
*3506	Unplasticized PVC pipe for industrial purposes	2.44.1
3601	Carbon steel pipes and tubes with specified room temperature properties for pressure purposes	5.AT.1
3656	Asbestos-cement pipes, joints and fittings for sewerage and drainage	2.33.1, 2.44.2
3690	Bitumens for building and civil engineering	
	Part 1: Bitumens for road purposes	3.8.1, 3.8.13, 3.8.15
3698	Calcium plumbate priming paints	2.94.6
3761	Solvent-based paint remover	2.94.7
3797	Lightweight aggregates for concrete	2.10.1, 2.10.2
3837	Expanded polystyrene boards	
	Part 1: Boards manufactured from expandable beads	2.98.1
3882	Recommendations and classification for top soil	2.4.1
3892	Pulverized-fuel ash	
	*Part 1: Pulverized-fuel ash for use as a cementitious component in structural concrete	2.14.2, 2.15.1
	*Part 2: Pulverized-fuel ash for use in grouts and for miscellaneous uses in concrete	2.14.1
*3921	Clay bricks	2.105.1
3936	Nursery stock	
	Part 1: Trees and shrubs	2.8.1
*3943	Plastics waste traps	2.39.3

BS	TITLE	REFERENCE(S)
3969	Recommendations for turf for general landscape purposes	2.5.1, 2.5(iii)
3998	Recommendations for tree work	3.10.3
4022	Prefabricated gypsum wallboard panels	2.98.1
*4027	Sulphate-resisting Portland cement	2.15.1, 4.15.1
4043	Recommendations for transplanting semi-mature trees	2.8.1, 3.10.2
4131	Terrazzo tiles	2.100.1
4165	Electrode wires and fluxes for the submerged arc welding of carbon steel and medium-tensile steel	2.71.3
4190	ISO metric black hexagon bolts, screws and nuts	2.72.1
4211	Ladders for permanent access to chimneys, other high structures, silos and bins	2.75.1, 2.75.3, 2.75.4
*4213	Cold water storage and feed and expansion cisterns (polyolefin or olefin copolymer) and cistern lids	2.40.1
4246	Low heat Portland-blastfurnace cement	
	Part 2: Metric Units	2.15.1
4248	Supersulphated cement	2.15.1
*4254	Two-part polysulphide-based sealants	2.125.4, 2.125(iii)
4320	Metal washers for general engineering purposes	2.72.1
4346	Joints and fittings for use with unplasticized PVC pressure pipes	
	*Part 1: Injection moulded unplasticized PVC fittings for solvent welding for use with pressure pipes, including potable water supply	2.32.2, 2.40.1
	*Part 2: Mechanical joints and fittings principally of unplasticized PVC	2.32.2, 2.40.1
	*Part 3: Solvent cements	2.32.5
4360	Weldable structural steels	2.44.1, 2.68.1, 2.69.1, 2.74.1, 6.20.1
4363	Distribution units for electricity supplies for construction and building sites	1.21(ii)
4375	Unsintered PTFE tape for thread sealing applications	2.41.1
4395	High strength friction grip bolts and associated nuts and washers for structural engineering	
	Part 1: General grade	2.72.1
	Part 2: Higher grade bolts and nuts and general grade washers	2.72.1
	Part 3: Higher grade bolts (waisted shank), nuts and general grade washers	2.72.1
4449	Carbon steel bars for the reinforcement of concrete	2.21.1, 2.122.1
4466	Bending dimensions and scheduling of bars for the reinforcement for concrete	4.21.1, 4.21.2
4471	Dimensions for softwood	2.85.2
4482	Cold reduced steel wire for the reinforcement of concrete	2.21.1
4483	Steel fabric for the reinforcement of concrete	2.21.1
4504	Flanges and bolting for pipes, valves and fittings. Metric series	
	Part 1: Ferrous	2.47.1, 2.47(ii), 2.72.2
*4514	Unplasticized PVC soil and ventilating pipe, fittings and accessories	2.39.1
4515	Process of welding of steel pipelines on land and offshore	5.AT.1
4551	Methods of testing mortars, screeds and plasters	9.13.3
4576	Unplasticized PVC rainwater goods	
	*Part 1: Half-round gutters and circular pipes	2.38.1
*4592	Industrial type metal flooring, walkways and stair treads	2.76.1, 2.76(i)
*4625	Prestressed concrete pressure pipes (including fittings)	2.30.1, 2.30(i)
4652	Metallic zinc-rich priming paint (organic media)	2.94.6
*4660	Unplasticized PVC underground drain pipe and fittings	2.32.3, 2.32.5, 2.44.2
4721	Ready-mixed building mortars	2.20.2, 2.20(i)

BS	TITLE	REFERENCE(S)
4729	Shapes and dimensions of special bricks	2.105.3
4756	Ready-mixed aluminium priming paints for woodwork	2.94.5
*4772	Ductile iron pipes and fittings	2.31.1, 2.31(ii), 2.47(ii)
4787	Internal and external wood doorsets, door leaves and frames	
	Part 1: Dimensional requirements	2.88.1
4800	Paint colours for building purposes	2.94.1
4841	Rigid urethane foam for building applications	
	Part 1: Laminated board for general purposes	2.98.1
	Part 2: Laminated board for use as a wall and ceiling insulation	2.98.1
4848	Hot-rolled structural steel sections	
	Part 2: Hollow sections	2.44.1, 2.68.1
	Part 4: Equal and unequal angles	2.68.1
4865	Dimensions of gaskets for pipe flanges to BS4504	
	Part 1: Dimensions of non-metallic gaskets for pressures up to 64 bar	2.48.1
*4873	Aluminium alloy windows	2.90.1
4880	Urinals	2.40.1
	Part 1: Stainless steel slab urinals	
*4887	Mortar admixtures	2.20.3
4928	Man-made fibre ropes	2.45.1
4933	ISO metric black cup and countersunk head bolts and screws with hexagon nuts	2.72.1
4942	Short link chain for lifting purposes	2.73.1, 2.73.2
	Part 2: Grade M(4) non-calibrated chain	
*4962	Plastics pipes for use as light sub-soil drains	2.43.1
4965	Decorative laminated plastics sheet veneered boards and panels	2.98.1
*4978	Timber grades for structural use	2.84.1, 2.84(ii)
4987	Coated macadam for roads and other paved areas	2.119.1, 3.8.4, 3.8.5, 3.8(iii), 8.5.1, 8.5(i)
4991	Propylene copolymer pressure pipe	2.37.1
5075	Concrete admixtures	
	Part 1: Accelerating admixtures, retarding admixtures and water reducing admixtures	2.16.1
	Part 2: Air-entraining admixtures	2.16.1
	Part 3: Super plasticizing admixtures	2.16.1
*5080	Methods of test for structural fixings in concrete and masonry	2.77.3, 2.77(iv)
5082	Water-borne priming paints for woodwork	2.94.5
5114	Performance requirements for joints and compression fittings for use with polyethylene pipes	2.40.1
5135	Process of arc welding of carbon and carbon manganese steels	5.AT.1
5150	Cast iron wedge and double disk gate valves for general purposes	2.49.1
5151	Cast iron gate (parallel slide) valves for general purposes	2.49.1
*5153	Cast iron check valves for general purposes	2.49.1
*5154	Copper alloy globe, globe stop and check, check and gate valves for general purposes	2.49.1
*5155	Butterfly valves	2.49.1
5156	Diaphragm valves for general purposes	2.49.1
5158	Cast iron and carbon steel plug valves for general purposes	2.49.1
*5163	Predominantly key-operated cast iron gate valves for waterworks purposes	2.49.1
*5178	Prestressed concrete pipes for drainage and sewage	2.30.1, 2.30(i)
*5212	Cold poured joint sealants for concrete pavements	2.125.3, 2.125(i)
5215	One-part gun-grade polysulphide-based sealants	2.125(iii)
5224	Masonry cement	2.15.1, 2.15(iii)

BS	TITLE	REFERENCE(S)
5236	Recommendations for the cultivation and planting of trees in the extra large nursery stock category	2.8.1, 3.10.1
*5254	Polypropylene waste pipe and fittings (external diameter 34.6mm, 41.0mm and 54.1mm)	2.39.1
*5255	Plastics waste pipe and fittings	2.39.1
5270	Polyvinyl acetate (PVAC) emulsion bonding agents for internal use with gypsum building plasters	2.95.2
5328	Methods for specifying concrete, including ready-mixed concrete	2.15(iii), 2.16(i), 2.63.2, 4.11, 4.2.3, 4.3.1, 4.3.2, 4.7(iii), 4.9.1, 4.10(ii), 4.10(iii)
*5358	Solvent-borne priming paint for woodwork	2.94.5
5391	Acrylonitrile-butadiene-styrene (ABS) pressure pipes	2.35.1
	Part 1: Pipe for industrial uses	
5392	Acrylonitrile-butadiene-styrene (ABS) fittings for use with ABS pressure pipes	
	Part 1: Fittings for use with pipe for industrial uses	2.35.1
5412 & 5413	Performance of draw-off taps with metal bodies for water services and with plastics bodies for water services	2.40.1
5433	Underground stopvalves for water services	2.40.1
5450	Sizes of hardwoods and methods of measurement	2.85.2
5480	Glass reinforced plastics (GRP) pipes and fittings for use for water supply or sewerage	2.34.1
*5481	Unplasticized PVC pipe and fittings for gravity sewers	2.32.3, 2.41.2, 2.44.2
5503	Vitreous china washdown WC pans with horizontal outlet	
	Part 1: Connecting dimensions	2.40.1
	Part 2: Materials, quality, performance and dimensions other than connecting dimensions	2.40.1
5520	Vitreous china bowl urinals. Rimless type	2.40.1
5627	Plastics connectors for use with horizontal outlet vitreous china WC pans	2.40.1
5642	Sills and copings	
	Part 1: Window sills of precast concrete, cast stone, clayware, slate and natural stone	2.91.1
	Part 2: Copings of precast concrete, cast stone, clayware, slate and natural stone	2.113.1
*5669	Wood chipboard and methods of test for particle board	2.87.2, 2.98.1
5709	Stiles, bridle gates and kissing gates	2.109.1, 2.109.2
5834	Surface boxes and guards for underground stopvalves for gas and waterworks purposes	
	Part 1: Guards, including foundation units	2.62.2, 2.62(i)
	*Part 2: Small surface boxes	2.62.2, 2.62(i)
	Part 3: Large surface boxes	2.62.2, 2.62(i)
5835	Recommendations for testing of aggregates	2.118.4
5889	Silicone based building sealants	2.125.5
5911	Precast concrete pipes and fittings for drainage and sewerage	
	*Part 2: Inspection chambers and street gullies	2.59.1, 8.14.2
	*Part 3: Ogee jointed concrete pipes, bends and junctions, unreinforced or reinforced with steel cages or hoops	2.28.1, 2.28(i), 2.43.1
	*Part 100: Unreinforced and reinforced pipes and fittings with flexible joints	2.28.1, 2.28(i), 2.30.2, 2.44.2, 2.63.6
	Part 101: Glass composite concrete (GCC) pipes and fittings with flexible joints	2.29.1, 2.29(ii)
	*Part 120: Reinforced jacking pipes with flexible joints.	5.24.5
	*Part 200: Unreinforced and reinforced manholes and soakaways of circular cross section	2.55.1, 2.55(i) 2.56.1

BS	TITLE	REFERENCE(S)
5977	Lintels	
	Part 1: Method of assessment of load	2.89(ii)
	*Part 2: Prefabricated lintels	2.89.1
6073	Precast concrete masonry units	2.105.1
6093	Design of joints and jointing in building construction	6.AT.2
*6076	Tubular polyethylene film for use as a protective sleeving for buried iron pipes and fittings	2.26.1, 2.26.2
*6087	Flexible joints for cast iron drainpipes and fittings (BS437) and for cast iron soil, waste and ventilating pipes and fittings (BS416)	2.38(iii), 2.39(i)
6178	Joist hangers	2.81.1
*6209	Solvent cement for non-pressure thermoplastics pipe systems	2.32.5
6213	Guide to the selection of constructional sealants	2.125(iv)
6323	Seamless and welded steel tubes for automobile, mechanical and general engineering purposes	
	Part 2: Specific requirements for hot finished welded steel tubes	2.44.1, 2.68.1, 2.74.1
	Part 3: Specific requirements for hot finished seamless tubes	2.68.1
	Part 4: Specific requirements for cold finished seamless steel tubes	2.68.1
	Part 5: Specific requirements for electric resistance and induction welded steel tubes	2.68.1
	Part 6: Specific requirements for cold finished electric resistance and induction welded steel tubes	2.68.1
	Part 7: Specific requirements for submerged arc welded steel tubes	2.68.1
	Part 8: Specific requirements for longitudinally welded stainless steel tubes	2.74.1
6398	Bitumen damp proof courses for masonry	2.127.1
6431	Ceramic floor and wall tiles	2.99.1, 2.99(i), 2.100.1
6446	Manufacture of glued structural components of timber and wood based panel products	6.19.2
6452	Beads for internal plastering and dry lining	2.97.1
6457	Reconstructed stone masonry units	2.112.2
*6510	Steel windows, sills, window boards and doors	2.90.1, 2.91.2
6515	Polyethylene damp-proof courses for masonry	2.127(i)
6566	Plywood	2.83.1
*6572	Blue polyethylene pipes up to nominal size 63 for below ground use for cold potable water	2.36.1, 2.40.1
6576	Installation of chemical damp-proof courses	6.4.1
6588	Portland pulverized-fuel ash cement	2.15.1
6610	Pozzolanic cement with pulverised-fuel ash as pozzolana	2.15.1, 2.15(iii)
6683	Guide to installation and use of valves	2.49(ii)
6699	Ground granulated blastfurnace slag for use with Portland cement	2.13.1, 2.15.1
6717	Precast concrete paving blocks	2.115.2
*6730	Black polyethylene pipes up to nominal size 63 for above ground use for cold potable water	2.36(ii)
6900	Raw, refined and boiled linseed oils for paints and varnishes	2.94.2
6920	Suitability of non-metallic products for use in contact with water intended for human consumption with regard to their effect on the quality of the water	
	Part 1: Specification	2.1(vi), 2.49.2
6925	Mastic asphalt for building and civil engineering (limestone aggregate)	2.101.1
6952	Exterior wood coating systems	6.26(i)

*—British Standards under which the BSI Certification Trade Mark is used. (See Clause 2.1)

APPENDIX III

List of British Standard Codes of Practice to which reference is made in the document

BS	TITLE	REFERENCE(S)
CP 102	Protection of buildings against water from the ground	6.4.1
CP 112	The structural use of timber	
	Part 3: Trussed rafters for roofs of dwellings	6.21.1, 6.21(i)
CP 144	Roof coverings	
	Part 3: Built-up bitumen felt	2.103(i), 6.28.1, 6.30.1
	Part 4: Mastic asphalt	2.103(i), 6.29.1
CP 202	Tile flooring and slab flooring	6.15.1
CP 204	In-situ floor finishes	
	Part 2: Metric Units	6.16.1
CP 312	Plastics pipework (thermoplastics materials)	5.1(i)
CP 413	Ducts for building services	2.44(i)
CP 1017	Distribution of electricity on construction and building sites	1.21(ii)
CP 1021	Cathodic protection	5.13(iii)
CP 2010	Pipelines	
	Part 2: Design and construction of steel pipelines in land	5.1(i)
5228	Code of practice for noise control on construction and demolition sites	1.AT.1
5262	Code of practice for external rendered finishes	6.17.1
5268	Structural use of timber	
	Part 2: Code of practice for permissible stress design, materials and workmanship	2.84.1
	Part 5: Preservative treatments for constructional timber	2.84.3
5385	Wall and floor tiling	6.18.1
5390	Code of practice for stone masonry	2.110(i)
5395	Stairs, ladders and walkways·	2.76(ii)
5449	Code of practice for central heating for domestic premises	6.32(i)
5492	Code of practice for internal plastering	6.12.4
5493	Code of practice for protective coating for iron and steel structures against corrosion	6.26.1
5534	Code of practice for slating and tiling	
	Part 1: Design	6.27.1
5589	Code of practice for preservation of timber	2.84.2
5606	Accuracy in building.	6.34.1
5607	Safe use of explosives in the construction industry	1.20.3, 3.13.4
5628	Use of masonry	
	Part 3: Materials and components, design and workmanship	2.17(i), 2.20(i) 6.1.1,6.1(i), 6.4.1
5837	Code of practice for trees in relation to construction	3.10.2, 3.10.4
5927	Laying of asbestos-cement pipelines	5.1(i)
5930	Code of practice for site investigations	1.AT.9(ii)
5955	Code of practice for plastics pipework (thermoplastics material)	5.1(i)
5975	Code of practice for falsework	4.17(i)
6031	Code of practice for earthworks	3.1(i)
6093	Design of joints and jointing in building construction	6.AT.2
6150	Code of practice for painting of buildings	2.94(i), 6.25(i) 6.25(ii), 6.26.1
6164	Safety in tunnelling in the construction industry	3.1(i)
6180	Protective barriers in and about buildings	2.74.1, 2.74(iii) 2.77(iii)
6187	Code of practice for demolition	3.AT.1
6262	Glazing for buildings	2.93(i), 6.25.1
6399	Design loading for buildings	
	Part 1: Code of practice for dead and inposed loads	2.74(i)

BS	TITLE	REFERENCE(S)
6657	Guide to prevention of inadvertent initiation of electro-explosive devices by radio-frequency radiation	3.13.3
6700	Design, installation, testing and maintenance of services supplying water for domestic use within buildings and their curtilages	6.32.1
6880	Code of practice for low temperature hot water heating systems of output greater than 45kW	6.32(i)
8004	Code of practice for foundations	3.AT.1
8005	Sewerage	
	Part 1: Guide to new sewerage construction	5.1(i), 5.19(i) 7.5(i), 7.6(i)
8007	Design of concrete structures for retaining aqueous liquids	2.10(v), 4.1(i), 4.5(i) 4.27(i), 7.13(i), 7.13(iii) 7.14(ii)
8010	Code of Practice for pipelines	5.1(i)
	Part 1: Pipelines on land: General	5.1(i)
	Section 2.1: Ductile Iron	5.1(i)
	Section 2.3: Asbestos-Cement	5.1(i)
	Section 2.4: Prestressed Concrete pressure pipelines	5.1(i)
8110	Structural use of concrete	2.15(iii), 2.15(v)
	Part 1: Code of practice for design and construction	2.16(i), 4.1(i), 4.2(iv) 4.3(iv), 4.3(vi), 4.7(ii) 4.8(i), 4.15(ii), 4.29(i)
8203	Code of practice for installation of sheet and tile flooring	6.15.1
8204	In-situ floorings	
	Part 2: Code of practice for concrete wearing surfaces	4.30.1, 6.14.1, 6.14(i)

APPENDIX IV

List of British Standard Special Issues to which reference is made in the document

PD	TITLE	REFERENCE(S)
6472	Guide to specifying the quality of building mortars	2.20(i)

APPENDIX V

List of British Standard Drafts for Development to which reference is made in the document

DD	TITLE	REFERENCE(S)
24	Recommendations for methods of protection against corrosion on light section steel used in building	6.26.1
69	Method for classifying the movement capability of sealants	2.125(iii)
121	Classification system for sealants for building and construction	2.125(iv)
140	Wall ties	
	Part 2: Recommendations for design of wall ties	2.106(i)

APPENDIX VI

List of Water Authorities Association (WAA) publications to which reference is made in the document

NUMBER	TITLE	REFERENCE(S)
Occasional Technical Papers		
1	A review of practice and recommendations in making connections to pipe sewers	5.22(i)
2	Water Supply Hygiene (Safeguards in the operation and management of public waterworks in England and Wales)	1.15.2, 1.15(i)
Health and Safety		
2	Safe working in sewers and at sewage works	1.17.1, 1.17(i)
4	Safe handling of chlorine and sulphur dioxide	1.16.1
Others	Water Authorities Association/Water Research Centre: Sewerage Rehabilitation Manual (Second Edition) 1986	9. General Note
	Principles of laying water mains	5.1(i)
	Principles of laying sewers	5.1(i)

APPENDIX VII

List of WAA Sewers and Water Mains Committee Water Industry specifications/Information and Guidance Notes to which reference is made in the document

Note: Water Industry specifications (WIs) have replaced Information and Guidance Notes (IGNs) and adopt the same numbering system – see 2.1(ii).

NUMBER	TITLE	REFERENCE(S)
4-08-01	Imported granular and selected as-dug and sidefill materials for buried pipelines	2.50.1
4-10-01	Bricks and mortar	2.20(ii), 2.105(ii)
4-11-01	Vitrified clay pipes and fittings	2.27(i)
4-12-01	Precast concrete pipes unreinforced and reinforced	2.28(iii)
4-12-02	Glass fibre strengthened concrete pipes	2.29(i)
4-12-03	Asbestos-cement pipes and fittings	2.33(i)
4-12-04	Specification for glassfibre reinforced cement (GRC) sewer linings	2.54.1
4-12-05	Specification for precast gunite sewer linings	2.54.1, 9.7.1
4-21-01	Ductile iron pipes and fittings	2.31(i)
4-22-01	Specification for compression fittings of copper and copper alloy for polyethylene pipes with outside diameters to BS 5556 (metric)	2.40.1
4-23-01	Selection, installation, operation and maintenance of isolating and boundary valves used in water distribution systems	2.49(iii)
4-31-01	Unplasticised PVC pipes and fittings	2.32(i), 5.8(iv)
4-31-02	Specification for plasticised PVC waterstops for use in construction and expansion joints in concrete retaining structures	2.126.1
4-31-03	Guide to joint design and installation of PVC waterstops in water retaining structures	2.126(ii)
4-31-05	Specification for solid wall concentric external rib-reinforced uPVC sewer pipe	2.32.4
4-32-03	Specification for blue polyethylene (PE) pressure pipe for cold potable water (nominal size 90 to 1000 for underground or protected use)	2.36.2
4-32-04	Specification for polyethylene socket and spigot fittings, saddles and drawn bends, for use with cold potable water (PE) pressure pipes	2.36.3
4-32-05	Specification for polyethylene (PE) pipes for sewer linings (non-pressure applications)	2.54.1
4-32-08	Specification for site fusion jointing of MDPE pipes and fittings	5.8.2
4-34-01	GRP pipes and fittings	2.34(i)
4-34-02	Specification for glassfibre reinforced plastics (GRP) sewer linings	2.54.1
4-34-04	Specification for polyester Insituform sewer linings	2.54.1
4-34-05	Specification for polyester resin concrete (PRC) sewer linings	2.54.1
4-40-01	Selection, properties, storage and installation requirements for elastomeric seals and sealing rings	2.46(i)
4-50-01	Operational guidelines for the loose polyethylene sleeving of underground iron mains	2.26(ii)
4-50-02	Operational guidelines for the transportation, handling and laying of ductile iron pipes with factory applied polyethylene sleeving	2.26(iii)
4-51-01	External zinc coating of ductile iron pipe	2.31(ii)
5-01-01	The United Kingdom Water Fitting Byelaws Scheme	2.40(iii)
5-01-03	Requirements for the testing of metallic materials for use in contact with potable water	2.1(vi), 2.49.2

* Copies of these documents can be obtained from the Librarian, WRc Swindon, PO Box 85, Frankland Road Blagrove, Swindon, Wilts. SN5 8YR. Telephone (0793) 511711.

APPENDIX VIII

List of Construction Industry Research and Information Association (CIRIA) publications to which reference is made in the document

NUMBER	TITLE	REFERENCE(S)
R44	Medical Code of Practice for Work in Compressed Air, 3rd Edition	1.18.1, 3.6.4
R59	Building Sands: availability, usage and compliance with specification requirements	2.12(i)
R67	Tables of minimum striking times for soffit and vertical formwork	4.19(i)
R73	Formwork striking times — methods of assessment	4.19(i)
R97	Trenching Practice	3.1(i)
TN71	A guide to the use of grass in hydraulic engineering practice	2.6(v)
TN75	Load tests on fixings in concrete	2.77(iv)
TN95	Proprietary trench support systems, 2nd Edition	3.1(i)
TN104	Precast concrete tunnel linings — review of current test procedures	2.63(ii)
TN128	Civil engineering sealants in wet conditions	2.125(vi)
G4	Selection and use of fixings in concrete and masonry	2.77(ii)
SP25	Site investigation manual	1.AT.9(ii)

APPENDIX IX

List of Parliamentary Acts and Regulations to which reference is made in the document.

TITLE	REFERENCE(S)
The Explosives Act 1875 and 1923	1.20(i)
The Petroleum (Consolidation) Act 1928	1.20(i)
The Petroleum Spirit (Motor Vehicles etc) Regulations 1929	1.20(i)
Public Health Act 1936	1.AT.13
Public Utilities Street Works Act 1950	3. General Note, 3.7(ii)
The Work in Compressed Air Special Regulations 1958	1.18(i)
The Construction (General Provisions) Regulations 1961	1.20(i), 1.At.3, 2.84(i)
Factories Act 1961	1.AT.8
The Construction (Health and Welfare) Regulations 1966	1.AT.8
The Construction (Working Places) Regulations 1966	1.AT.7
The Highly Flammable Liquids and Liquefied Petroleum Gases Regulations 1972	1.20(i)
Control of Pollution Act 1974	1.14(ii), 1.AT.1
Health and Safety at Work etc Act 1974	1.AT.1
Salmon and Fresh Water Fisheries Act 1975	1.14(ii)
Fire Certificates (Special Premises) Regulations 1976	1.AT.12
Land Drainage Act 1976	1.14(ii)
Highways Act 1980	3.8(i)
The Health and Safety (First Aid) Regulations 1981	1.AT.5
Wildlife and Countryside Act 1981	1.7(ii), 2.6(vi)

APPENDIX X

List of Miscellaneous Publications to which reference is made in the document.

NUMBER	TITLE	REFERENCE(S)
	Traffic Signs Manual – Department of Transport	1.3(ii), 1.12.1, 1.AT.4
Advice Note TD/21/85	Portable Traffic Signals at Roadworks on Single Carriageway Roads – Department of Transport	1.12.1
Advice Note TA/47/85	Control of Traffic at Roadworks on Single Carriageway Roads – Department of Transport	1.12.1
Advice Note TA/6/80	Traffic Signs and safety measures for minor works on minor roads – Department of Transport	1.12.1
	Traffic Warning Signs for Roadworks – Department of Transport	1.12(i)
	Regulations for Electrical Installations, 15th Edition – Institution of Electrical Engineers	1.21.1, 1.12(i), 1.21(ii) 6.AT.1
	Guidance on the Preparation, Submission and Consideration of Tenders for Civil Engineering Contracts – Institution of Civil Engineers Conditions of Contract Standing Joint Committee	1.AT.9(iii)
	The Water Industry's Duty under the Health and Safety at Work etc Act to Contractors Employed by the Industry – National Joint Health and Safety Committee Employers' Side	1.AT.15
	Water Fittings and Materials Directory – Water Research Centre	2.1(v)
	Statement of the Committee on Chemicals and Materials of Construction for Use in Public Water Supply and Swimming Pools – Department of the Environment	2.1(v)
TR 30	Alkali – silica Reaction – Minimising the Risk of Damage to Concrete-Concrete Society	2.10(iii), 2.15(vi), 4.3(v)
Digest 330	Alkali – silica Reaction – Building Research Establishment	2.10(iii), 2.15(vi), 4.3(v)
Publication 978	Technical Criteria for Wood Windows – British Woodworking Federation	2.90.1
Digest 276	Hardcore – Building Research Establishment	2.116(i)
LR 90	Frost Susceptibility of Soils and Road Materials – Transport and Road Research Laboratory	2.117.2
	Specification for Highway Works – Department of Transport	2.124.1, 3.12(i), 8.General Note
	Specification for Piling: Contract Documentation and Measurement – Institution of Civil Engineers	3.AT.2
	Design of normal concrete mixes – Department of the Environment	4.3(vii)
	Guides to practice in corrosion control – No. 9 Cathodic Protection – National Corrosion Service of the National Physical Laboratory.	5.13(ii)
	A Guide to Pipe Jacking Design – Pipe Jacking Association	5.24(ii)

APPENDIX XI

DETAILS OF PROBLEM/COMPLAINT UPON QUALITY ASSURED PRODUCTS

1. Name of complainant ....

2. The product and specification reference ....

   ....

3. Name of manufacturer ....

4. Details of the product i.e. size, type, class, date of manufacture (if known), batch number (if known) etc.

   ....

   ....

   ....

5. How many items appear unsatisfactory? ....

6. How many items were ordered? ....

7. Were quality assured products ordered?   YES/NO

8. Were all the products delivered, marked with a mark of conformity?   YES/NO

9. Date the products were delivered ....

10. When was the problem identified? ....

11. Were the products supplied by: the manufacturer/a merchant

12. With which clauses of the specification do the products appear not to comply:

    Nos. ....

13. Details of problem/complaint ....

    ....

    ....

14. Has the manufacturer been advised of the problem?   YES/NO

15. If yes to 14 what was the response? ....

    ....

16. If no to 14, do you wish us to reveal to the manufacturer that you are the complainant?   YES/NO

17. Have the products all been installed?   YES/NO

18. Do you wish the products to be examined on Site by a certification body representative?   YES/NO

19. If yes to 18 please give details of Site location and name of contact.
    (We shall arrange a mutually convenient date to visit the site.)

INDEX TO SPECIFICATION